C000119439

Section One — Numbers

Order of Operations P.1

Q1
a) 8
b) 5
c) 6.56
d) 11.22
e) -0.90
f) 319.98
g) 5.5
h) 983
i) 9.17
j) 0

Q2
a) 8
b) 73
c) 113
d) 7
e) 22.57
f) 8.67
g) 1
h) 1.42
i) -488.76
j) -0.26

Q3
a) 3
b) 0.1
c) 16
d) 8.33
e) -0.01
f) 70.88
g) -176.95
h) 0.21
i) 0.58
j) 0.27
k) 0.01
l) -10.64

Types of Number P.2

Q1 4

Q2 -3 °C

Q3
a) $6 \div 2 = 3$, rational
b) $\sqrt{16} = 4$, rational
c) $\sqrt{5} = 2.23606...$, irrational
d) $3 \div 8 = 0.375$, rational
e) $\sqrt[3]{25} = 2.92401...$, irrational
f) Rational

Q4
a) the third cube number (27)
b) the fourth square number (16)

Q5
a) 2
b) e.g. 29
c) 19
d) 19 and 2
e) e.g. 1 or 25

Q6 a)

1	②	③	4	⑤	6	⑦	8	9	10
⑪	12	⑬	14	15	16	⑰	18	⑲	20
21	22	㉓	24	25	26	27	28	㉙	30
㉛	32	33	34	35	36	㊲	38	39	40
㊶	42	㊸	44	45	46	㊼	48	49	50
51	52	㊾	54	55	56	57	58	㊾	60
㊱	62	63	64	65	66	㊿	68	69	70
㉛	72	㊂	74	75	76	77	78	㊃	80
81	82	㊃	84	85	86	87	88	㊉	90
91	92	93	94	95	96	㊆	98	99	100

b) 3 of: 11 (11), 13 (31), 17 (71), 37 (73), 79 (97)
c) e.g. 3 is a factor of 27

Q7 113

Q8 There's just one: 2 is the only even prime.

Square Roots and Cube Roots P.3

Q1
a) 7.7
b) 4.4
c) 5.8
d) 14.1
e) 22.8
f) 8.7
g) 27.4
h) 0.9
i) 13.0
j) 85.0
k) 1000.0
l) 5.2

Q2
a) 2 and –2
b) 4 and –4
c) 3 and –3
d) 7 and –7
e) 5 and –5
f) 10 and –10
g) 12 and –12
h) 8 and –8
i) 9 and –9

Q3
a) 16
b) 12
c) 11
d) 100
e) 1
f) 0.5

Q4
a) 4
b) 8
c) 5
d) 10
e) 6
f) 20

Q5 7 cm

Q6 240 m

Q7 4

Multiples, Factors and Prime Factors P.4-P.5

Q1
a) 12
b) 3
c) 1, 9
d) 1, 3, 9
e) P = 12, Q = 6

Q2 Any 5 of:
2 groups of 24, 3 groups of 16,
4 groups of 12, 6 groups of 8,
8 groups of 6, 12 groups of 4,
16 groups of 3, 24 groups of 2.

Q3 The Conversational French and Woodturning classes both have a prime number of pupils and so cannot be divided into equal groups.

Q4
a) 1, 8, 27, 64, 125
b) 8, 64
c) 27
d) 8, 64
e) 125

Q5
a) 2×3^2
b) $2^2 \times 5 \times 7$
c) 47

Q6
a) 2, 3, 5, 7, 11
b) 28
c) $2^2 \times 7$

Q7
a) 1, 3, 5, 7, 9
b) 25
c) 5^2

Q8
a) 495
b) $3 \times 5 \times 11$

Q9
a) 1, 4, 9, 16, 25, 36, 49, 64, 81, 100
b) 4, 16, 36, 64, 100
c) 9, 36, 81
d) 1, 64
e) Total = 385 = $5 \times 7 \times 11$

Q10
a) $50 \times 25 \times 16 = 20,000$ cm³
b) $2^5 \times 5^4$
c) 200. It is not enough to divide the large volume by the smaller volume as the shapes of the blocks are important too. It is possible to fit $16 \div 4 = 4$ small blocks across the width, $50 \div 5 = 10$ small blocks along the length and $25 \div 5 = 5$ small blocks down the height of the large block. This enables Gordon to fit $4 \times 10 \times 5 = 200$ small blocks into the big block

Q11
a) 680
b) $2^2 \times 5 \times 17$
c) $2 \times 5 \times 17$
d) 5×17

Q12 42

LCM and HCF P.6

Q1
a) 6, 12, 18, 24, 30, 36, 42, 48, 54, 60
b) 5, 10, 15, 20, 25, 30, 35, 40, 45, 50
c) 30

Q2
a) 1, 2, 3, 5, 6, 10, 15, 30
b) 1, 2, 3, 4, 6, 8, 12, 16, 24, 48
c) 6

Q3
a) 20
b) 10
c) 2
d) 15
e) 15
f) 5
g) 32
h) 16
i) 16

Q4
a) 120
b) 120
c) 120
d) 45
e) 90
f) 180
g) 64
h) 192
i) 192

Q5
a) 7th June
b) 16th June
c) Sunday (1st July)
d) Lars

Fractions P.7-P.9

Q1
a) $\frac{1}{64}$
b) $\frac{1}{9}$
c) $\frac{1}{18}$
d) $3\frac{29}{32}$
e) $5\frac{5}{32}$
f) $\frac{81}{100\,000}$

Q2
a) 1
b) 4
c) $\frac{1}{2}$
d) $\frac{2}{5}$
e) $\frac{10}{33}$
f) 1000

Q3
a) $\frac{1}{4}$
b) $\frac{5}{6}$
c) $\frac{1}{2}$
d) $4\frac{3}{8}$
e) $5\frac{3}{8}$
f) 1

Q4 $3\frac{7}{15}$, so the bowl will be big enough.

Q5
a) 0
b) $\frac{1}{2}$
c) $-\frac{1}{6}$
d) $1\frac{7}{8}$
e) $-3\frac{1}{8}$
f) $\frac{4}{5}$

Answers: P.7 – P.16

Q6 a) $\frac{3}{4}$ b) $\frac{5}{12}$ c) $\frac{7}{15}$

     d) $4\frac{3}{4}$ e) 4   f) $1\frac{1}{5}$

     g) $\frac{5}{8}$ h) $-\frac{1}{24}$ i) $4\frac{3}{5}$

     j) $1\frac{1}{30}$ k) 1   l) $\frac{44}{75}$

Q7 a) 1/12   b) 1/4   c) 2/3

Q8 a) 3/4 of the programme
     b) 5/8 of the programme
     c) 1/8 of the programme

Q9 3/5 of the kitchen staff are girls.
     2/5 of the employees are boys.

Q10 7/30 of those asked had no opinion.

Q11 a) 12/30 = 2/5
     b) 6 days

Q12 a) Each box will hold 16 sandwiches.
       So 5 boxes will be needed for 80
       sandwiches.
     b) 25 inches tall

Q13 a) $\frac{1}{18}$ b) $\frac{1}{4}$

Q14 a) 48 km²   b) $\frac{5}{8}$

Q15 a) 8 people   b) $\frac{7}{20}$

     c) $\frac{1}{4}$ d) 57 people

     e) 65 people

Q16 After the 1st bounce the ball reaches
     4 m, after the 2nd $2\frac{2}{3}$ m, after the 3rd
     $1\frac{7}{9}$ m.

Q17 a) 100 g flour   b) 350 g

     c) $\frac{2}{7}$ d) 300 g

Q18 £31.06

Fractions, Decimals and Percentages P.10-P.11

Q1 a) 25%   e) 41.52%
     b) 50%   f) 84.06%
     c) 75%   g) 39.62%
     d) 10%   h) 28.28%

Q2 a) 0.5   e) 0.602
     b) 0.12   f) 0.549
     c) 0.4   g) 0.431
     d) 0.34   h) 0.788

Q3 a) 50%   e) 4%
     b) 25%   f) 66.7%
     c) 12.5%   g) 26.7%
     d) 75%   h) 28.6%

Q4 a) 1/4   e) 41/500
     b) 3/5   f) 62/125
     c) 9/20   g) 443/500
     d) 3/10   h) 81/250

Q5 85%

Q6 Grade C

Q7 a) 0.3   e) 1.75
     b) 0.37   f) 0.125
     c) 0.4   g) 0.6
     d) 0.375   h) 0.05

Q8

Fraction	Decimal
1/2	0.5
1/5	0.2
1/8	0.125
8/5	1.6
4/16	0.25
7/2	3.5
x/10	0.x
x/100	0.0x
3/20	0.15
9/20	0.45

Q9 a) $0.8\dot{3}$ e) $0.\overline{90}$

     b) $0.\dot{7}$ f) $0.\overline{460317}$

     c) $0.\overline{63}$ g) $0.\overline{478}$

     d) $0.4\overline{7}$ h) $0.5\overline{891}$

Q10 a) $\frac{3}{5}$ e) $\frac{1}{3}$

     b) $\frac{3}{4}$ f) $\frac{2}{3}$

     c) $\frac{19}{20}$ g) $\frac{1}{9}$

     d) $\frac{16}{125}$ h) $\frac{16}{99}$

Q11 a) $\frac{2}{9}$ e) $\frac{4}{33}$

     b) $\frac{4}{9}$ f) $\frac{545}{999}$

     c) $\frac{8}{9}$ g) $\frac{251}{333}$

     d) $\frac{80}{99}$ h) $\frac{52}{333}$

Percentages P.12-P.14

Q1 a) £1.28   b) 629 kg
     c) 16 mins

Q2 a) 0.2   c) 0.02
     b) 0.35   d) 0.625

Q3 a) $\frac{1}{5}$ c) $\frac{7}{10}$

     b) $\frac{3}{100}$ d) $\frac{421}{500}$

Q4 a) 12.5%   c) 30%
     b) 23%   d) 34%

Q5 85%

Q6 72.5%

Q7 a) £4275   b) £6840

Q8 1.6%

Q9 500%

Q10 £358.80

Q11 £244.40

Q12 23 028

Q13 Car 1 costs £8495 – (0.15 × £8495)
     = £8495 – £1274.25 = £7220.75.
     Car 2 costs £8195 – (0.12 × £8195)
     = £8195 – £983.40 = £7211.60.
     So car 2 is the cheapest.

Q14 £5980

Q15 £152.75, So NO, he couldn't afford it.

Q16 31%

Q17 13%

Q18 a) 67.7%   b) 93.5%
     c) 38.1%

Q19 £80

Q20 a) 300   b) 4 whole years

Q21 £236.25

Q22 38%

Q23 Final cost of stereo
     = $x \times (1 + 0.35) \times (1 - 0.2) = x \times 1.08$
     So, the shop's overall profit is 8%.

Q24 House value now
     = $y \times (1 + 0.1) \times (1 - 0.05)$
     = $y \times 1.045$
     So, if they sell now they will make a
     profit of 4.5%.

Interest and Depreciation P.15

Q1 a) £473.47   c) £779.42
     b) £612.52   d) £1065

Q2 Splitting the investment. £2.21 better.

Q3 a) £7877.94   d) £10 646.54
     b) £27 116.06   e) £7184.25
     c) £9980.90   f) £5843.70

Q4 a) 4% compound interest gives £1040
       5% simple interest gives £1050
       £5 a month gives £1060
       £5 a month account pays more.
     b) 4% compound interest gives
       £4440.73
       5% simple interest gives £4500
       £5 a month gives £3600
       5% simple interest pays more.
     c) 4% compound interest gives
       £5864.84
       5% simple interest gives £4950
       £5 a month gives £3700
       4% compound interest pays more.

Q5 a) £270   d) £8012
     b) £790   e) £5100
     c) £1130

Ratios P.16-P.17

Q1 a) 3:4   d) 9:16
     b) 1:4   e) 7:2
     c) 1:2   f) 9:1

Q2 a) 6 cm   d) 1.5 cm
     b) 11 cm   e) 2.75 cm
     c) 30.4 m   f) 7.6 m

Q3 a) £8, £12
     b) 80 m, 70 m
     c) 100 g, 200 g, 200 g.
     d) 1hr 20 m, 2 hr 40 m, 4 hrs.

Q4 John 4, Peter 12

IGCSE
Mathematics
for Edexcel

The Answer Book

Includes **Free** Online Edition

For the Edexcel International GCSE

Contents

How to get your free Online Edition

This book includes a **free** Online Edition you can read on your computer or tablet. To access it, just go to **cgpbooks.co.uk/extras** and enter this code...

2350 7572 6123 7409

By the way, this code only works for one person. If somebody else has used this book before you, they might have already claimed the Online Edition.

Published by CGP

ISBN: 978 1 84762 556 4

www.cgpbooks.co.uk

Printed by Elanders Ltd, Newcastle upon Tyne.
Clipart from Corel®

Q5 400 ml, 600 ml, 1000 ml

Q6 30

Q7 Jane £40, Holly £48, Rosemary £12

Q8 Paul — £16

Q9 a) 245 girls   b) 210 boys

Q10 a) £39   b) £140

Q11 a) 1:300   b) 6 m
    c) 3.3 cm

Q12 a) 15 kg   b) 30 kg
    c) 8 kg cement, 24 kg sand and 48 kg gravel.

Q13 a) 30 fine   b) 15 not fine
    c) 30/45 = 2/3

Q14 a) 45 Salt & Vinegar
    b) 90 bags sold altogether

Proportion P.18

Q1 85

Q2 £247.80

Q3 112 hrs

Q4 £96.10

Q5 96 sheep

Q6 a) 9.33 cm   b) 30.45 km

Q7 a) 400 g
    b) 300 g
    c) She will need 350 g of butter so she doesn't have enough.

Q8 44 cows

Q9 a) 55.3 cm   c) 20.4 °C
    b) 51.5 cm   d) 19.5 °C

Rounding Numbers P.19-P.20

Q1 a) 62.2   b) 62.19
    c) 62.194   d) 19.62433
    e) 6.300   f) 3.142

Q2 a) 1330   b) 1330
    c) 1329.6   d) 100
    e) 0.02   f) 0.02469

Q3 a) 457.0   b) 456.99
    c) 456.987   d) 457
    e) 460   f) 500

Q4 2.83

Q5 a) 0.704 (to 3 s.f. — the least number of significant figures used in the question).
    b) 3.25 (to 3 s.f. — the least number of significant figures used in the question).

Q6 a) £1100   d) £3
    b) £88   e) £376
    c) £300   f) £44

Q7 23 kg

Q8 £5.07

Q9 235 km

Q10 £19

Q11 £4.77

Q12 235 cm

Q13 470 cm

Q14 1810 g

Q15 13 s

Estimating P.21

Q1 Mark's tank is approximately 4500 cm³, so it won't be big enough.

Q2 a) $6500 \times 2 = 13\,000$
    b) $8000 \times 1.5 = 12\,000$
    c) $40 \times 1.5 \times 5 = 300$
    d) $45 \div 9 = 5$
    e) $35\,000 \div 7000 = 5$
    f) $\frac{55 \times 20}{10} = 55 \times 2 = 110$
    g) $7000 \times 2 = 14\,000$
    h) $100 \times 2.5 \times 2 = 500$
    i) $20 \times 20 \times 20 = 8000$
    j) $8000 \div 80 = 100$
    k) $62\,000 \div 1000 = 62$
    l) $3 \div 3 = 1$

Q3 Approximately $15\,000 - (1500 + 2500 + 1500 + 1500 + 3000) = 5000$

Q4 a) $\frac{150 + 50}{150 - 50} = \frac{200}{100} = 2$
    b) $\frac{20 \times 10}{\sqrt{400}} = \frac{200}{20} = 10$
    c) $\frac{2000 \times 4}{20 \times 5} = \frac{8000}{100} = 80$
    d) $\frac{10^2 \div 10}{4 \times 5} = \frac{10}{20} = 0.5$

Q5 a) $2 \times (3 \times 3) + 2 \times (2 \times 3.5) = 36$ m²
    b) 3 tins

Q6 a) 6.9 (accept 6.8)
    b) 10.9 (accept 10.8)
    c) 9.2 (accept 9.1)
    d) 4.1 (accept 4.2)
    e) 9.9 (accept 9.8)
    f) 5.8 (accept 5.9)

Bounds P.22-P.23

Q1 a) 64.785 kg   b) 64.775 kg

Q2 a) 1.75 m
    b) $1.85 \times 0.75 = 1.3875$ m²

Q3 a) 2.525 l   b) 2.475 l

Q4 a) 95 g
    b) Upper bound = 97.5 g, lower bound = 92.5 g.
    c) No, since the lower bound for the electronic scales is 97.5 g, which is greater than the upper bound for the scales in part a).

Q5 a) Upper bound = 13.5, lower bound = 12.5.
    b) Upper bound = 12.55, lower bound = 12.45.

    c) To calculate the upper bound for C multiply the upper bound for A by the upper bound for B; $13.5 \times 12.55 = 169.425$
    To calculate the lower bound for C multiply the lower bound for A by the lower bound for B; $12.5 \times 12.45 = 155.625$

Q6 a) Upper bound = 5 minutes 32.5 seconds, lower bound = 5 minutes 27.5 seconds.
    b) The lower bound for Jimmy's time is 5 minutes 25 seconds, which is lower than the lower bound for Douglas' time (5 minutes 25.5 seconds).

Q7 a) Upper bound = 945, lower bound = 935.
    b) Upper bound = 5.565, lower bound = 5.555.
    c) To find the upper bound for R, divide the upper bound for S by the lower bound for T; $945 \div 5.555 = 170.117...$
    To find the lower bound for R, divide the lower bound for S by the upper bound for T; $935 \div 5.565 = 168.014...$
    d) $940 \div 5.56 = 170$ (to 2 s.f. — the upper and lower bounds both round to 170 to 2 s.f., but give different answers to 3 s.f.).

Q8 At least 18.2 m²

Q9 The upper bound for the distance is 127.5 km. The lower bound for the time is 1 hour and 45 minutes = 1.75 hours. The maximum value of the average speed is $127.5 \div 1.75 = 72.857...$ km/hour.

Q10 a) Perimeter = $2(12 + 4) = 32$ cm. Maximum possible error = 4×0.1 cm = 0.4 cm.
    b) Maximum possible error in P is $2(x + y)$.

Standard Form P.24-P.25

Q1 a) 35.6   b) 3560
    c) 0.356   d) 35600
    e) 8.2   f) 0.00082
    g) 0.82   h) 0.0082
    i) 1570   j) 0.157
    k) 157000   l) 15.7

Q2 a) 2.56×10^0 b) 2.56×10
    c) 2.56×10^{-1} d) 2.56×10^4
    e) 9.52×10 f) 9.52×10^{-2}
    g) 9.52×10^4 h) 9.52×10^{-4}
    i) 4.2×10^3 j) 4.2×10^{-3}
    k) 4.2×10 l) 4.2×10^2

Answers: P.24 – P.31

Q3 **a)** 3.47×10^2 **b)** 7.3004×10
c) 5×10^0 **d)** 9.183×10^5
e) 1.5×10^7 **f)** 9.371×10^6
g) 7.5×10^{-5} **h)** 5×10^{-4}
i) 5.34×10^0 **j)** 6.2103×10^2
k) 1.49×10^4 **l)** 3×10^{-7}

Q4 6×10^{-3}

Q5 1×10^9, 1×10^{12}

Q6 9.46×10^{12}

Q7 6.9138×10^4

Q8 1.2×10^{-2} (mm)

Q9 **a)** Mercury
b) Jupiter
c) Mercury
d) Neptune
e) Venus and Mercury
f) Jupiter, Neptune and Saturn

Q10 **a)** 6×10^9 **e)** 5.6×10^{16}
b) 1.89×10^7 **f)** 3.99×10^4
c) 4×10^4 **g)** 4.3473×10^6
d) 2×10^2 **h)** 1.748×10^4

Q11 **a)** 2.4×10^{10}
b) 1.6×10^6
c) 1.8×10^5

Q12 1.04×10^{13} is greater by 5.78×10^{12}

Q13 1.3×10^{-9} is smaller by 3.07×10^{-8}

Q14 **a)** 4.2×10^7 **b)** 3.8×10^{-4}
c) 1.0×10^7 **d)** 1.12×10^{-4}
e) 8.43×10^5 **f)** 4.232×10^{-3}
g) 1.7×10^{18} **h)** 2.83×10^{-4}
i) 1×10^{-2}

Q15 7×10^6

Q16 6.38×10^8 cm

Q17 3.322×10^{-27} kg

Q18 **a)** 1.8922×10^{16} m
b) 4.7305×10^{15} m

Q19 **a)** 510000000 km^2
b) 3.62×10^8 km^2
c) 148000000 km^2

Sets and Venn Diagrams P.26-P.27

Q1 **a)** E = {prime numbers less than 12}
b) E = {2, 3, 5, 7, 11}

Q2 **a)** L **b)** E.g. $1 \in K$ and $1.1 \notin K$

Q3 **a)** B = {-3, 1, 7, 8, 9, 12, 21}
b)

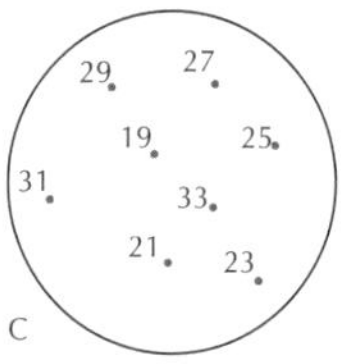

Q4 **a)**

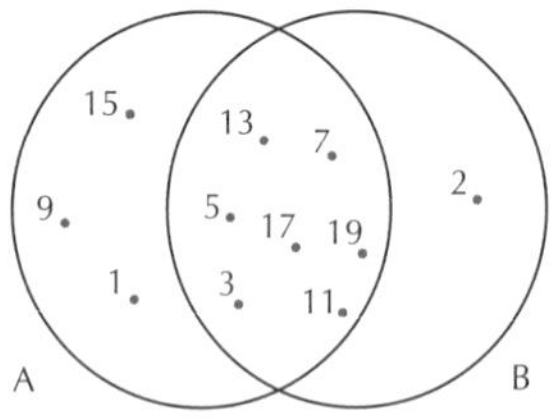

b)

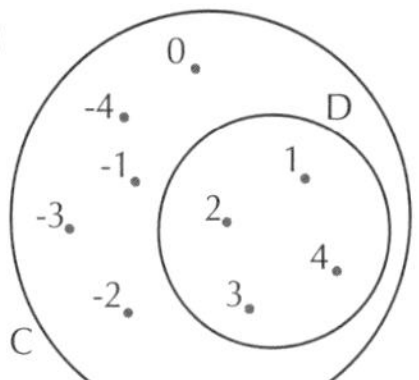

Q5 **a)** R = {1, 8, 27, 64}
b) n(S) = 9
c) $R \cap S$ = {1, 64}
d) $n(R \cup S) = 11$

Q6 **a)** People who answered the survey
b) 9
c) $n(D \cup P) = 58$ and $n(D \cap P) = 3$

Q7 **a)** All the cows he counted
b) 19
c) n(P) = 83
d) $n(C \cup G) = 59$
e) $n(C') = 80$
f) $n(C \cap P) = 25$
g) $n(C \cap G \cap P) = 11$
h) $n(G \cap P \cap C') = 23$

Q8 **a)** false **g)** true
b) false **h)** false
c) true **i)** true
d) false **j)** false
e) false **k)** true
f) false **l)** false

Section Two — Algebra

Sequences P.28

Q1 **a)** 10, 12, 14; even numbers
b) 9, 11, 13; odd numbers
c) 25, 36, 49; square numbers
d) 125, 216, 343; cube numbers

Q2 **a)** 31, 36, 41 **b)** 5
c) 5n + 1 **d)** 101

Q3 **a)** 2n **b)** 2n – 1
c) 5n **d)** 3n + 2

Q4 **a)** 19, 22, 25, $3n + 4$
b) 32, 37, 42, $5n + 7$
c) 46, 56, 66, $10n - 4$
d) 82, 89, 96, $7n + 47$

Q5 No.

Q6 **a)** 4n – 3
b) 75 is not in the sequence because when the expression is set to equal 75, n is not a whole number.

Q7 24, 35, 48

Q8 **a)** $16\frac{7}{8}$, $16\frac{9}{16}$, $16\frac{23}{32}$, $16\frac{41}{64}$
b) The 10th term will be the mean of the 8th and 9th terms.

Powers and Roots P.29-P.31

Q1 **a)** 16
b) 1000
c) $3 \times 3 \times 3 \times 3 \times 3 = 243$
d) $4 \times 4 \times 4 \times 4 \times 4 \times 4 = 4096$
e) $1 \times 1 \times 1 \times 1 \times 1 \times 1 \times 1 \times 1 \times 1 = 1$
f) $5 \times 5 \times 5 \times 5 \times 5 \times 5 = 15\,625$

Q2 **a)** 2^8 (or 256)
b) 12^5 (or 248 832)
c) x^5 **d)** m^3
e) y^4 **f)** z^6

Q3 **b)** 10^7 **c)** 10^6
d) 10^8
e) Simply add the powers.

Q4 **b)** 2^3 **c)** 4^2
d) 8^3
e) Simply subtract the powers.

Q5 **a)** true **b)** true
c) false **d)** false
e) true **f)** false
g) false **h)** true
i) false **j)** true
k) true **l)** false

Q6 **a)** 3^{-3} **d)** 3^{-12}
b) 4^{25} **e)** 4^6
c) 10^{-13} **f)** 5^3

Q7 **a)** 275 **b)** 0.123
c) 53 400 **d)** 6.40×10^{-5}
e) 2.37 **f)** 2.31
g) 10.4 **h)** 0.843
i) 2.25 **j)** 2.18
k) 0.244 **l)** 0.965

Q8 **a)** 8.76 **b)** 4.17
c) 19.4 **d)** 219
e) 108 **f)** 91.9
g) 13.6 **h)** 17.8
i) 5.06

Q9 **a)** 0.008 **b)** 0.25
c) 1.53×10^{-5} **d)** 0.667
e) 2.24 **f)** 1.82
g) 1.55 **h)** 2.60
i) 0.512 **j)** 1.21
k) 0.0352 **l)** 7.28

Q10 **a)** 1.49 **b)** 20.1
c) 2.50 **d)** 6.55
e) 1.08 **f)** 8.78
g) 0.707 **h)** –0.380

Q11 **a)** 9.14 **b)** 1.50
c) 0.406 **d)** 476
e) 0.0146 **f)** 1.22
g) 84.5 **h)** 0.496
i) 165 **j)** 8.47

Q12 **a)** $k \times k$
b) $p \times p \times p \times q \times q$
c) $g \times t \times t$
d) $g \times g \times t \times t$
e) $-t \times -t$
f) $-(t \times t)$

Q13 **a)** a^3 **d)** c^3d^2
b) c^5 **e)** $4x^3$
c) a^2b^3 **f)** $6xy^3$

Answers: P.31 – P.35

Q14 a) x^5 **m)** u^3
b) x **n)** 1
c) $-y^{13}$ **o)** gt
d) q^3 **p)** 1
e) b^9 **q)** k^{10}
f) $x^3 + x^2$ **r)** p^6
g) $-f^7$ **s)** v^2
h) x^7y^7 **t)** i
i) p^9q^6 **u)** g^7t^{14}
j) $-x$ **v)** x^{11}
k) 1 **w)** r^3
l) 1

Q15 a) $\dfrac{1}{k^2}$ **d)** y^2

b) $\dfrac{q^2}{p^3}$ **e)** a^4v^2

c) $\dfrac{g}{t^2}$ **f)** $\dfrac{a^4}{bv^2}$

Q16 a) $\dfrac{1}{h^6}$ **d)** $\dfrac{1}{v^2}$

b) $\dfrac{1}{g^3}$ **e)** $\dfrac{1}{w}$

c) $\dfrac{1}{t^4}$ **f)** $\dfrac{1}{a^4}$

Q17 a) $3a^3$ **f)** $\dfrac{1}{6j^2}$

b) p^4q^5 **g)** $\dfrac{b^{\frac{7}{10}}}{8}$

c) x^3y^4 **h)** $\dfrac{3}{u^{\frac{1}{2}}}$

d) x^2 **i)** $10d^{\frac{1}{8}}$

e) $2x^{\frac{1}{2}}$

Algebra Basics P.32

Q1 a) -27°C **d)** +18°C
b) -22°C **e)** +15°C
c) +12°C **f)** -12°C

Q2 Expression **b)** is larger by 1.

Q3 a) $-4x$ **b)** $18y$

Q4 a) $-1000, -10$ **c)** $144, 16$
b) $-96, -6$ **d)** $0, 0$

Q5 -4

Q6 a) $-6xy$ **g)** $\dfrac{-5x}{y}$

b) $-16ab$ **h)** 3

c) $8x^2$ **i)** -4

d) $-16p^2$ **j)** -10

e) $\dfrac{10x}{y}$ **k)** $4x$

f) $\dfrac{-10x}{y}$ **l)** $-8y$

Q7 a) $15x^2 - x$
b) $13x^2 - 5x$
c) $-7x^2 + 12x + 12$
d) $30abc + 12ab + 4b$
e) $18pq + 8p$

---

f) $17ab - 17a + b$
g) $4pq - 5p - 9q$
h) $16x^2 - 4y^2$
i) $abc + 10ab - 11cd$
j) $-2x^2 + y^2 - z^2 + 6xy$

Q8 a) $x^2 + 4x + 3x + 12 = x^2 + 7x + 12$
b) $4x^2 + 6x + 6x + 9 = 4x^2 + 12x + 9$
c) $15x^2 + 3x + 10x + 2$
$= 15x^2 + 13x + 2$

Formulas from Words P.33

Q1 a) $y = x + 5$ **d)** $y = x + 6^2$
b) $y = 7x + 4$ **e)** $y = x^2 \div 8$
c) $y = (x - 7) \div 3$ **f)** $y = x^2 \div 12$

Q2 a) $c = 25n$
b) $c = (25 + 1.25)n = 26.25n$

Q3 a) $N = n + 23$ **d)** $N = xn$
b) $N = n - 14$ **e)** $N = nx^2$
c) $N = 2n$

Q4 a) i) $4d$ cm **ii)** d^2 cm²
b) i) $a + b + c$ cm **ii)** $\frac{1}{2}cz$ cm²

Q5 $C = 10 + 5h$

Q6 $T = (73 + 27)p + 15l = 100p + 15l$

Q7 $S = (3 + \frac{1}{3}w)d$

Multiplying Out Brackets P.34

Q1 a) $4x + 4y - 4z$
b) $x^2 + 5x$
c) $-3x + 6$
d) $9a + 9b$
e) $-a + 4b$
f) $2x - 6$
g) $4e^2 - 2f^2 + 10ef$
h) $16m - 8n$
i) $6x^2 + 2x$
j) $-2ab + 11$
k) $-2x^2 - xz - 2yz$
l) $3x - 6y - 5$
m) $-3a - 4b$
n) $14pqr + 8pq + 35qr$
o) $x^3 + x^2$
p) $4x^3 + 8x^2 + 4x$
q) $8a^2b + 24ab + 8ab^2$
r) $7p^2q + 7pq^2 - 7q$
s) $16x - 8y$

Q2 a) $x^2 - 2x - 3$
b) $x^2 + 2x - 15$
c) $x^2 + 13x + 30$
d) $x^2 - 7x + 10$
e) $x^2 - 5x - 14$
f) $28 - 11x + x^2$
g) $6x - 2 + 9x^2 - 3x = 9x^2 + 3x - 2$
h) $6x^2 - 12x + 4x - 8 = 6x^2 - 8x - 8$
i) $4x^2 + x - 12x - 3 = 4x^2 - 11x - 3$
j) $4x^2 - 8xy + 2xy - 4y^2$
$= 4x^2 - 4y^2 - 6xy$
k) $12x^2 - 8xy + 24xy - 16y^2$
$= 12x^2 - 16y^2 + 16xy$
l) $9x^2 + 4y^2 + 12xy$

Q3 $15x^2 + 10x - 6x - 4 = 15x^2 + 4x - 4$

Q4 $4x^2 - 4x + 1$

Q5 a) $(4x + 6)$ m
b) $(-3x^2 + 17x - 10)$ m²

Q6 a) $(8x + 20)$ cm
b) $40x$ cm²
c) $40x - 12x = 28x$ cm²

Q7 a) Perimeter — $3x + 29$ cm
Area — $\dfrac{7x + 126}{2}$ cm²
b) Perimeter — $(8x + 4)$ cm
Area — $(3x^2 + 14x - 24)$ cm²
c) Perimeter — $(16x - 4)$ cm
Area — $(16x^2 - 8x + 1)$ cm²
d) Perimeter — $(10x + 4)$ cm
Area — $(6x^2 - 5x - 6)$ cm²

Factorising P.35

Q1 a) $a^2(b + c)$
b) $a^2(5 + 13b)$
c) $a^2(2b + 3c)$
d) $a^2(a + y)$
e) $a^2(2x + 3y + 4z)$
f) $a^2(b^2 + ac^2)$

Q2 a) $x(x - 5)$
b) $2(x + 3)$
c) $3x(x + 4)$
d) $2x(2x - 3)$
e) $3xy(1 + 4x)$
f) $3(3x + 5)$
g) $5x(3xy - 5)$
h) $4pq(q - 5 + 2p)$
i) $2x(5x^3 + 3)$
j) $5x^2(3x - 4)$
k) $7x(3x + 2)$
l) $5xy(z + 4u)$

Q3 a) $4xyz(1 + 2) = 12xyz$
b) $4xyz(2 + 3) = 20xyz$
c) $8xyz(1 + 2x)$
d) $4xyz^2(5xy + 4)$

Q4 a) $(x + 3)(x - 3)$
b) $(y + 4)(y - 4)$
c) $(5 + z)(5 - z)$
d) $(6 + a)(6 - a)$
e) $(2x + 3)(2x - 3)$
f) $(3y + 2)(3y - 2)$
g) $(5 + 4z)(5 - 4z)$
h) $(1 + 6a)(1 - 6a)$
i) $(x^2 + 6)(x^2 - 6)$
j) $(x^2 + y^2)(x^2 - y^2)$
k) $(1 + ab)(1 - ab)$
l) $(10x + 12y)(10x - 12y)$

Q5 a) $(x + 2)(x - 2)$
b) $(12 + y^2)(12 - y^2)$
c) $(1 + 3xy)(1 - 3xy)$
d) $(7x^2y^2 + 1)(7x^2y^2 - 1)$

Q6 a) $16a^2b^2(4b - a)$
b) $q(p + r - pqr)$
c) $3(m^2 - 8)$
d) $b^2(b^2 - ab + c)$
e) $(a^2 - 13)(a^2 + 13)$

Answers: P.35 – P.41

f) $3ab(3b - c)$
g) $(9 - z)(9 + z)$
h) $(6m - 5n)(6m + 5n)$
i) $mn(m + 3 - 2n^2)$
j) $(11p - 3q)(11p + 3q)$
k) $12(12x^2 - 9y^2 - 5z^2)$
l) $(8ab - 7cd)(8ab + 7cd)$

Manipulating Surds P.36

Q1 **a)** $\sqrt{15}$ **d)** x
   b) 2 **e)** 8
   c) x **f)** $\sqrt{5}$

Q2 3π cm²

Q3 **a)** 1 **e)** $3\sqrt{5}$
   b) $5\sqrt{3}$ **f)** $5\sqrt{2}$
   c) $2\sqrt{2}$ **g)** $\sqrt{2}$
   d) $7 + 4\sqrt{3}$ **h)** $3(\sqrt{2} - 1)$

Q4 **a)** $(1 + \sqrt{5})(1 - \sqrt{5}) = -4$, rational
   b) $\frac{1 + \sqrt{5}}{1 - \sqrt{5}} = -\frac{1}{2}(3 + \sqrt{5})$, irrational

Q5 **a)** $(x + y)(x - y) = -1$, rational
   b) $\frac{x + y}{x - y} = -3 - 2\sqrt{2}$, irrational

Q6 **a)** $\frac{\sqrt{2}}{2}$ **e)** $\sqrt{2} - 1$
   b) $\frac{\sqrt{2}}{2}$ **f)** $3 - \sqrt{3}$
   c) $\frac{\sqrt{10}a}{10}$ **g)** $\frac{2[\sqrt{6} - 1]}{5}$
   d) $\frac{\sqrt{xy}}{y}$ **h)** $\frac{3 + \sqrt{5}}{2}$

Q7 $3\sqrt{3}$

Q8 $\sqrt{16} \times \sqrt{2} + 3\sqrt{2} = 7\sqrt{2}$

Q9 $19 + 6\sqrt{2}$

Solving Equations P.37-P.38

Q1 1

Q2 **a)** $x = \pm3$ **d)** $x = \pm3$
   b) $x = \pm6$ **e)** $x = \pm1$
   c) $x = \pm3$

Q3 **a)** $x = 5$ **d)** $x = -6$
   b) $x = 4$ **e)** $x = 5$
   c) $x = 10$ **f)** $x = 9$

Q4 **a)** $x = 5$ **e)** $x = 6$
   b) $x = 2$ **f)** $x = 5$
   c) $x = 8$ **g)** $x = \pm2$
   d) $x = 17$

Q5 **a)** 15.5 cm   **b)** 37.2 cm

Q6 £15.50

Q7 **a)** $x = 9$ **g)** $x = 15$
   b) $x = 2$ **h)** $x = 110$
   c) $x = 3$ **i)** $x = \pm6$
   d) $x = 3$ **j)** $x = 66$
   e) $x = 4$ **k)** $x = 700$
   f) $x = -1$ **l)** $x = 7\frac{1}{2}$

Q8 **a)** Joan — £x
   Kate — £$2x$
   Linda — £$(x - 232)$
   b) $4x = 2632$
   $x = 658$
   c) Kate — £1316
   Linda — £426

Q9 **a)** $2x + 32$ cm
   b) $12x$ cm²
   c) $x = 3.2$

Q10 **a)** $x = 0.75$ **d)** $x = -1$
   b) $x = -1$ **e)** $x = 4$
   c) $x = -6$ **f)** $x = 13$

Q11 $x = 8$

Q12 $x = 1$

Q13 8 yrs

Q14 39, 35, 8

Q15 **a)** $y = 22$ **f)** $x = 7$
   b) $x = 8$ **g)** $x = \pm3$
   c) $z = -5$ **h)** $x = \pm4$
   d) $x = 19$ **i)** $x = \pm7$
   e) $x = 23$

Q16 $x = 1\frac{1}{2}$

Q17 **a)** $x = 5$ **b)** $x = 9$

Q18 $x = 1\frac{1}{2}$ AB = 5 cm
   AC = 5½ cm
   BC = 7½ cm

Rearranging Formulas P.39-P.40

Q1 **a)** $h = \frac{10 - g}{4}$ **b)** $c = 2d - 4$
   c) $k = 3 + \frac{j}{2}$ **d)** $b = \frac{3a}{2}$
   e) $g = \frac{8f}{3}$ **f)** $x = 2(y + 3)$
   g) $t = 6(s - 10)$ **h)** $q = \pm\frac{\sqrt{p}}{2}$

Q2 **a)** $c = \frac{w - 500m}{50}$
   b) 132

Q3 **a) i)** £38.00   **ii)** £48.00
   b) $c = 28 + 0.25n$
   c) $n = 4(c - 28)$
   d) i) 24 miles **ii)** 88 miles
   iii) 114 miles

Q4 **a)** $x = \pm\sqrt{y + 2}$
   b) $x = y^2 - 3$
   c) $s = \pm 2\sqrt{r}$
   d) $g = 3f - 10$
   e) $z = 5 - 2w$
   f) $x = \pm\sqrt{\frac{3v}{h}}$
   g) $a = \frac{v^2 - u^2}{2s}$
   h) $u = \pm\sqrt{v^2 - 2as}$
   i) $g = \frac{4\pi^2 l}{t^2}$

Q5 **a)** £Jx **b)** $P = T - Jx$
   c) $J = \frac{T - P}{x}$ **d)** £16

Q6 **a) i)** £2.04   **ii)** £3.48
   b) C = $(12x + 60)$ pence
   c) $x = \frac{C - 60}{12}$
   d) i) 36   **ii)** 48   **iii)** 96

Q7 **a)** $x = \frac{z}{y + 2}$
   b) $x = \frac{b}{a - 3}$
   c) $x = \frac{y}{4 - z}$
   d) $x = \frac{3z + y}{y + 5}$
   e) $x = \frac{-2}{y - z}$ or $\frac{2}{z - y}$
   f) $x = \frac{2y + 3z}{2 - z}$
   g) $x = \frac{-y - wz}{yz - 1}$ or $\frac{y + wz}{1 - yz}$
   h) $x = \frac{-z}{4}$

Q8 **a)** $p = \frac{4r - 2q}{q - 3}$
   b) $g = \frac{5 - 2e}{f + 2}$
   c) $b = \frac{3c + 2a}{a - c}$
   d) $q = \pm\sqrt{\frac{4}{p - r}} = \pm\frac{2}{\sqrt{p - r}}$
   e) $a = \frac{2c + 4b}{4 + c - d}$
   f) $x = \pm\sqrt{\frac{-3y}{2}}$
   g) $k = \pm\sqrt{\frac{14}{h - 1}}$
   h) $x = \left(\frac{4 - y}{2 - z}\right)^2$
   i) $a = \frac{b^2}{3 + b}$
   j) $m = -7n$
   k) $e = \frac{d}{50}$
   l) $y = \frac{x}{3x + 2}$

Q9 **a)** $y = \frac{x}{x - 1}$
   b) $y = \frac{-3 - 2x}{x - 1}$ or $\frac{2x + 3}{1 - x}$
   c) $y = \pm\sqrt{\frac{x + 1}{2x - 1}}$
   d) $y = \pm\sqrt{\frac{1 + 2x}{3x - 2}}$

Factorising Quadratics P.41

Q1 **a)** $(x + 5)(x - 2)$
   $x = -5, x = 2$
   b) $(x - 3)(x - 2)$
   $x = 3, x = 2$
   c) $(x - 1)^2$
   $x = 1$
   d) $(x - 3)(x - 1)$
   $x = 3, x = 1$
   e) $(x - 5)(x + 4)$
   $x = 5, x = -4$
   f) $(x + 1)(2x - 5)$
   $x = -1, x = \frac{5}{2}$

Answers: P.41 – P.47

g) $(3x + 7)(x - 1)$
$x = -\frac{7}{3}, x = 1$
h) $(x + 7)^2$
$x = -7$
i) $(x - 5)(2x + 3)$
$x = 5, x = -\frac{3}{2}$

Q2 **a)** $(x + 9)(x - 4)$
$x = -9, x = 4$
b) $x(x - 5)$
$x = 0, x = 5$
c) $(x - 7)(x + 3)$
$x = 7, x = -3$
d) $(x - 24)(x - 2)$
$x = 24, x = 2$
e) $(x + 7)(x - 2)$
$x = -7, x = 2$
f) $(x - 6)(x + 3)$
$x = 6, x = -3$

Q3 $x = \frac{1}{2}, x = -\frac{1}{2}$

Q4 **a)** $(x^2 - x)$ m^2
b) $x = 3$

Q5 **a)** $x(x + 1)$ cm^2
b) $x = 3$

Q6 **a)** x^2 m^2
b) $12x$ m^2
c) $x^2 + 12x - 64 = 0$
$x = 4$

Q7 **a)** area $= l(l - 0.75)$ cm^2
b) i) area $= (16l^2 - 12l)$ cm^2
ii) $16l^2 - 12l - 340 = 0 \Rightarrow l = 5$

Q8 **a)** $\frac{4}{x + 5}$ **b)** $\frac{x + 2}{x - 3}$
c) $\frac{2x + 3}{3x + 1}$

The Quadratic Formula P.42-P.43

Q1 **a)** 1.87, 0.13
b) 2.39, 0.28
c) 1.60, - 3.60
d) 1.16, -3.16
e) 0.53, -4.53
f) -11.92, -15.08
g) -2.05, -4.62
h) 0.84, 0.03

Q2 **a)** -2, -6 **b)** 0.67, -0.5
c) 3, -2 **d)** 2, 1
e) 3, 0.75 **f)** 3, 0
g) 0.67 **h)** 0, -2.67
i) 4, -0.5 **j)** 4, -5
k) 1, -3 **l)** 5, -1.33
m) 1.5, -1 **n)** -2.5, 1
o) 0.5, 0.33 **p)** 1, -3
q) 2, -6 **r)** 2, -4

Q3 **a)** 0.30, -3.30 **b)** 3.65, -1.65
c) 0.62, -1.62 **d)** -0.55, -5.45
e) -0.44, -4.56 **f)** 1.62, -0.62
g) 0.67, -4.00 **h)** -0.59, -3.41
i) 7.12, -1.12 **j)** 13.16, 0.84
k) 1.19, -4.19 **l)** 1.61, 0.53
m) 0.44, -3.44 **n)** 2.78, 0.72

Q4 **a)** 1.7, -4.7 **b)** -0.27, -3.73
c) 1.88, -0.88 **d)** 0.12, -4.12
e) 4.83, -0.83 **f)** 1.62, -0.62
g) 1.12, -1.79 **h)** -0.21, -4.79
i) 2.69, -0.19 **j)** 2.78, 0.72
k) 1, 0 **l)** 1.5, 0.50

Q5 $x^2 - 3.6x + 3.24 = 0$
$x = 1.8$

Q6 **a)** $x^2 + 2.5x - 144.29 = 0$
$x = 10.83$
b) 48.3 cm

Algebraic Fractions P.44-P.45

Q1 **a)** $\frac{3xy}{z}$ **c)** $\frac{1}{3xy^2z^3}$
b) $\frac{12b^2}{c}$ **d)** $\frac{q^3}{2r^3}$

Q2 **a)** $\frac{2}{xy}$ **g)** $\frac{x^3}{5}$
b) $\frac{3a^2b}{2}$ **h)** $\frac{12a^3b^2}{5}$
c) $\frac{y}{2x^2}$ **i)** $\frac{3a^4c^3}{2bd}$
d) $\frac{2qr^2}{3}$ **j)** 1
e) $\frac{8x^2z^2}{y}$ **k)** $\frac{3rt^2}{2}$
f) $\frac{90ac^4}{b}$ **l)** $\frac{d^6}{e^3f}$

Q3 **a)** $2x^2y$ **g)** $\frac{12yz}{x}$
b) a **h)** $\frac{4a^3}{b}$
c) $\frac{3x^2}{y}$ **i)** $\frac{5a^3}{b}$
d) $\frac{pq}{2}$ **j)** $\frac{2x}{y^2z}$
e) $2ef$ **k)** $\frac{6}{n}$
f) $5x^3$ **l)** $\frac{7g}{f}$

Q4 **a)** $\frac{3a - 4}{2}$ **b)** $\frac{2x - y}{4}$
c) $\frac{5x + 6}{3}$

Q5 **a)** $x = 5$
b) $x = 2$

Q6 **a)** $\frac{3 + y}{2x}$ **g)** $\frac{3x + 2 + y}{24}$
b) $\frac{1 + y}{x}$ **h)** $\frac{x + 2y - 2}{10}$
c) $\frac{2xy}{z}$ **i)** $\frac{7x}{6}$
d) $\frac{6x + 1}{3}$ **j)** $\frac{37x}{42}$
e) $\frac{7x + 6}{x}$ **k)** $\frac{x(y + 3)}{3y}$
f) $\frac{14x + y}{6}$ **l)** $\frac{xyz + 4x + 4z}{4y}$

Q7 **a)** $\frac{4x - 5y}{3}$ **g)** $\frac{z}{15}$
b) $\frac{4x - 1}{y}$ **h)** $\frac{m(12 - n)}{3n}$
c) $\frac{4x + 3y - 2}{2x}$ **i)** $\frac{b(14 - a)}{7a}$
d) $\frac{2 - 2x}{x}$ **j)** $\frac{-p + 5q}{10}$
e) $\frac{-1}{4x}$ **k)** $\frac{-3p - 4q}{4}$
f) $\frac{4x - y}{6}$ **l)** $\frac{9x - 4y + xy}{3y}$

Q8 **a)** $\frac{a^2}{b^2}$ **f)** $\frac{11}{6x}$
b) 1 **g)** $\frac{2(a^2 + b^2)}{a^2 - b^2}$
c) $\frac{3}{2r}$ **h)** $\frac{3}{4}$
d) $\frac{mn(pm + 1)}{p^2}$ **i)** $\frac{3x - 6y}{8}$
e) $\frac{2x}{x^2 - y^2}$

Inequalities P.46-P.47

Q1 **a)** $9 \le x < 13$
b) $-4 \le x < 1$
c) $x \ge -4$
d) $x < 5$
e) $x > 25$
f) $-1 < x \le 3$
g) $0 < x \le 5$
h) $x < -2$

Q2 **a)** – **h)** number lines

Q3 **a)** $x > 3$ **b)** $x < 4$
c) $x \le 5$ **d)** $x \le 6$
e) $x \ge 7.5$ **f)** $x < 4$
g) $x < 7$ **h)** $x < 4$
i) $x \ge 3$ **j)** $x > 11$
k) $x < 3$ **l)** $x \ge -\frac{1}{2}$
m) $x \le -2$ **n)** $x > 5$
o) $x < 15$ **p)** $x \ge -2$

Q4 Largest integer for x is 2.

Q5 $\frac{11 - x}{2} < 5, x > 1$

Q6 $1130 \le 32x$
36 classrooms are needed.

Q7 50 guests (including bride and groom), $900 \ge 18x$

SECTION TWO — ALGEBRA

Answers: P.47 – P.52

Q8 $x \geq 2,$ $y > 1,$ $x + y \leq 5$

Q9

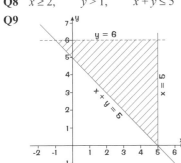

Q10 a)
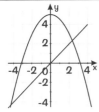
b)
c)
d)
e)
f)
g)
h)

Q11 a) $x > 5,$ $y \geq 7,$ $x + y \geq 14$

b)

Simultaneous Equations and Graphs P.48

Q1 a) $x = 3, y = 3$ b) $x = 2, y = 5$
c) $x = 1, y = 2$ d) $x = 1, y = 2$
e) $x = 1, y = 4$ f) $x = 1, y = 2$
g) $x = 2, y = 3$ h) $x = 2, y = 3$
i) $x = 5, y = 2$ j) $x = 3, y = 4$

Q2 a) $x = 0, x = 1$
b) $x = 2.7, x = -0.7$
c) $x = 3.4, x = -2.4$
d) $x = 1.6, x = -2.6$
e) $x = 0.7$
f) $x = 3.4, x = -2.4$
g) $x = 1.6, x = -2.6$

Q3

x	-4	-3	-2	-1	0	1	2	3	4
$-\frac{1}{2}x^2$	-8	-4.5	-2	-0.5	0	-0.5	-2	-4.5	-8
+5	5	5	5	5	5	5	5	5	5
y	-3	0.5	3	4.5	5	4.5	3	0.5	-3

a) $x = 3.2, x = -3.2$
b) $x = 4, x = -4$
c) $x = 2.3, x = -4.3$

Simultaneous Equations P.49

Q1 a) $x = 4, y = 18$ OR $x = -3, y = 11$
b) $x = 6, y = 28$ OR $x = -3, y = 1$
c) $x = 1.5, y = 4.5$ OR $x = -1, y = 2$
d) $x = -3, y = 33/5$ OR $x = 2, y = \frac{28}{5}$
e) $x = -\frac{1}{4}, y = \frac{17}{4}$ OR $x = -3, y = 40$
f) $x = -\frac{2}{3}, y = \frac{31}{3}$ OR $x = -4, y = 57$

Q2 a) $x = 1, y = 2$
b) $x = 0, y = 3$
c) $x = -1\frac{1}{2}, y = 4$
d) $x = 5, y = 23$ OR $x = -2, y = 2$
e) $x = \frac{1}{3}, y = -\frac{29}{3}$ OR $x = 4, y = 38$
f) $x = \frac{1}{2}, y = -\frac{3}{2}$ OR $x = -2, y = 6$
g) $x = 1, y = 9$
h) $x = 8, y = -\frac{1}{2}$
i) $x = -1, y = 3$

Q3 a) $6x + 5y = 430$
$4x + 10y = 500$
b) $x = 45, y = 32$

Q4 7 chickens
4 cats

Q5 5 g (jellies are 4 g)

Q6 $3y + 2x = 18$
$y + 3x = 6$ $x = 0, y = 6$
$4y + 5x = 7$
$2x - 3y = 12$ $x = 3, y = -2$
$4x - 6y = 13$
$x + y = 2$ $x = 2\frac{1}{2}, y = -\frac{1}{2}$

Q7 $5m + 2c = 344$
$4m + 3c = 397$
$m = 34p, c = 87p$

Q8 $x = 12, y = 2$

Direct and Inverse Proportion P.50

Q1 $y = 20$

Q2 $y = 184.8$

Q3 $y = 2$

Q4 $x = 2$

Q5

x	1	2	3	4	5	6
y	48	24	16	12	9.6	8

Q6

x	1	2	5	10
y	100	25	4	1

x	2	4	6	8
y	24	6	$2^2/_3$	1.5

Q7 4 kg

Q8 a) $r = 96$ b) $s = 4$
c) $r = 600$ d) $s = -8$

Q9 9.5 N kg⁻¹

Section Three — Graphs, Functions and Calculus

Coordinates P.51-P.52

Q1

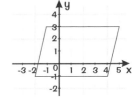

missing coordinate = (5, 3)

Q2

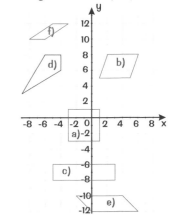

a) B is (1, -3)   b) C is (5, 5)
c) A is (-5, -8)   d) D is (-4, 6)
e) D is (0, -12)   f) C is (-3, 12)

Q3

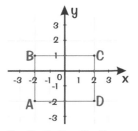

C = (2, 1), D = (2, -2)

Q4

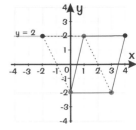

Possible coordinates = $(-2, 2)$ and $(4, 2)$.

Q5 a) (3,4)   b) (5.5,5)
c) (5.5,11)   d) (8.5,9)
e) (3,3.5)   f) (9.5,9.5)
g) (20,41.5)   h) (30.5,20.5)

Q6 (110, 135)

Q7 a) (2,5.5)   b) (0.5,1.5)
c) (2,–2.5)   d) (1,–1)
e) (2,3)   f) (4,–0.5)
g) (–13,–12.5) h) (–5,–7)

Answers: P.53 – P.57

Straight-Line Graphs P.53-P.54

Q1
a) B   f) F
b) A   g) C
c) F   h) B
d) G   i) D
e) E   j) H

Q2

x	-4	-3	-2	-1	0	1	2	3	4
3x	-12	-9	-6	-3	0	3	6	9	12
-1	-1	-1	-1	-1	-1	-1	-1	-1	-1
y	-13	-10	-7	-4	-1	2	5	8	11

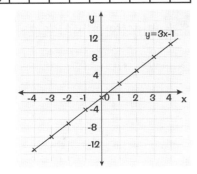

Q3

x	-6	-4	-2	0	2	4	6
1/2 x	-3	-2	-1	0	1	2	3
-3	-3	-3	-3	-3	-3	-3	-3
y	-6	-5	-4	-3	-2	-1	0

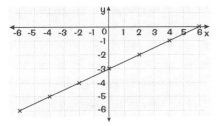

Q4

x	0	3	8
y	3	9	19

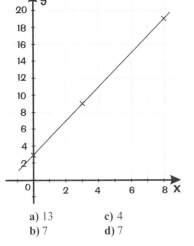

a) 13   c) 4
b) 7   d) 7

Q5

x	-8	-4	8
y	-5	-4	-1

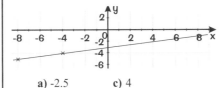

a) -2.5   c) 4
b) -3   d) 6

Q6

Number of Units used	0	100	200	300
Cost using method A	10	35	60	85
Cost using method B	40	45	50	55

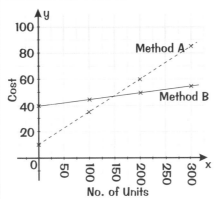

a) i) £27.50   ii) £43.50
b) Method A
c) 150 units

Finding the Gradient P.55

Q1
a) $-\frac{1}{2}$ g) 4
b) 3   h) 1
c) $-\frac{1}{4}$ i) -1
d) -2   j) $\frac{1}{3}$
e) $-\frac{2}{3}$ k) $-\frac{1}{2}$
f) $-\frac{8}{3}$ l) 3

Q2
a) 2   d) -2
b) $\frac{1}{2}$ e) $\frac{1}{2}$
c) -1   f) $-\frac{3}{4}$

Q3
a) A and C
b) (1, 2)

Q4 The gradient is -0.23 so it's a red run.

"y = mx + c" P.56

Q1
a) $m = 4$, (0, 3)
b) $m = 3$, (0, -2)
c) $m = 2$, (0, 1)
d) $m = -3$, (0, 3)
e) $m = 5$, (0, 0)
f) $m = -2$, (0, 3)
g) $m = -6$, (0, -4)
h) $m = 1$, (0, 0)
i) $m = -\frac{1}{2}$, (0, 3)
j) $m = \frac{1}{4}$, (0, 2)
k) $m = \frac{4}{3}$, (0, 2)

Q2
a) $y = \frac{7}{2}x - 1$ d) $y = \frac{1}{4}x - 3$
b) $y = \frac{1}{2}x + 4$ e) $y = -\frac{1}{2}x$
c) $y = -\frac{1}{5}x + 7$ f) $y = -2x - 6$

Q3
a) $y = x + 4$ c) $y = -x$
b) $y = 3x + 2$ d) $y = -3x + 4$

Q4
a) $y = x$ c) $y = -3x + 3$
b) $y = 3x$ d) $y = -2x - 4$

Q5
a) $x = 4$ c) $y = 7$
b) $x = 8$ d) $y = 9$

Q6 (7, 20) and (5, 14)

Quadratic Graphs P.57

Q1

x	-4	-3	-2	-1	0	1	2	3	4
$y=2x^2$	32	18	8	2	0	2	8	18	32

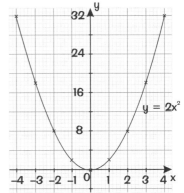

Q2

x	-4	-3	-2	-1	0	1	2	3	4
x^2	16	9	4	1	0	1	4	9	16
$y=x^2+x$	12	6	2	0	0	2	6	12	20

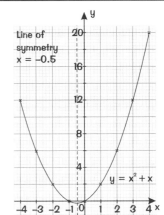

Line of symmetry $x = -0.5$

$y = x^2 + x$

Answers: P.57 – P.62

Q3 a)

x	-4	-3	-2	-1	0	1	2	3	4
3	3	3	3	3	3	3	3	3	3
$-x^2$	-16	-9	-4	-1	0	-1	-4	-9	-16
$y=3-x^2$	-13	-6	-1	2	3	2	-1	-6	-13

b)

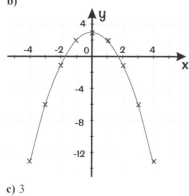

c) 3

Harder Graphs P58-P61

Q1
a) Reciprocal   f) Reciprocal
b) Reciprocal   g) Straight line
c) Reciprocal   h) Cubic
d) Quadratic   i) Cubic
e) Quadratic   j) Cubic

Q2
a) ix   g) viii
b) iv   h) vi
c) iii   i) x
d) vii   j) v
e) xi   k) ii
f) xii   l) i

Q3

x	-3	-2	-1	0	1	2	3
$y=x^3$	-27	-8	-1	0	1	8	27

Q4

x	-3	-2	-1	0	1	2	3
$y=-x^3$	27	8	1	0	-1	-8	-27

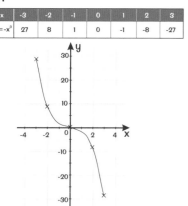

Q5

x	-3	-2	-1	0	1	2	3
x^3	-27	-8	-1	0	1	8	27
$y=x^3+4$	-23	-4	3	4	5	12	31

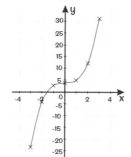

Q6

x	-3	-2	-1	0	1	2	3
$-x^3$	27	8	1	0	-1	-8	-27
$y=-x^3-4$	23	4	-3	-4	-5	-12	-31

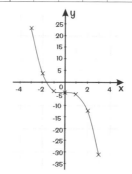

Q7 The graph has been moved 4 units up the y-axis.

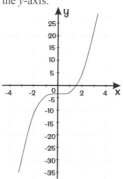

Q8 The graph has been moved 4 units down the y-axis.

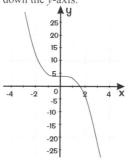

Q9

x	-4	-3	-2	-1	0	1	2	3	4
$y=1/x$	-0.25	-0.33	-0.5	-1	n/a	1	0.5	0.33	0.25

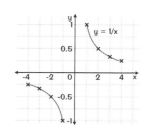

Q10

x	-4	-3	-2	-1	0	1	2	3	4
x^2	16	9	4	1	0	1	4	9	16
$y=3/x^2$	0.2	0.3	0.8	3	0	3	0.8	0.3	0.2

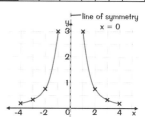

Q11

x	-4	-3	-2	-1	0	1	2	3	4
$y=2^x$	0.06	0.1	0.3	0.5	1	2	4	8	16

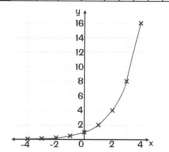

c) Anything to the power of 0 is 1.

Q12

x	-3	-2	-1	0	1	2	3
3^x	0.04	0.1	0.3	1	3	9	27
$6/x$	-2	-3	-6	n/a	6	3	2
$y=3^x-6/x$	2.04	3.1	6.03		-3	6	25

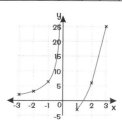

Functions P.62

Q1
a) f(x) = 3 + x
b) f(x) = 790 − 41x
c) f(x) = 3(9x² + 2)

Q2
a) x = 4.5   d) x = ±2
b) x = ±1   e) x = 0.27 or -7.27
c) x = ±0.31   f) x = 5

Q3
a) x > 4   d) x < -3.5
b) x ≤ 0   e) x = -0.75
c) x = 0

Q4 a) f(8) = 44
b) g(3) = -6
c) f(-4) = -4
d) gf(x) = 3 − (4x + 12)²
e) fg(x) = 4(3 − x^2) +12
f) gf(2) = -397

Q5 a) h⁻¹(x) = x − 6
b) f⁻¹(x) = $\frac{11}{x}$ − 1
c) g⁻¹(h(x)) = $\frac{4}{3}$(6 + x)
d) f⁻¹(g(x)) = $\frac{44}{3x}$ − 1
e) h⁻¹(f(5)) = -4$\frac{1}{6}$
f) h⁻¹(g(-1)) = -6.75

Q6 a) f(-1) = -$\frac{2}{3}$ **d)** n⁻¹(2) = -14.5
b) g(9) = 554 **e)** 12
c) kj(-3) = 210 **f)** 0.75

Q7 a) hi(x) = (11 ÷ (-x + $\frac{x^2}{2}$)) − 8
b) m⁻¹(x) = $\frac{10(x-3)+4}{18}$ = $\frac{5x-9}{9}$
c) p⁻¹(q(x)) = $\frac{(\frac{13}{x-2})-5}{8}$ = $\frac{23-5x}{8x-16}$

Differentiation P63-P66

Q1 a) 4x^3 **g)** 2x^3
b) 2x **h)** 33
c) 13x^{12} **i)** 1
d) 4x **j)** 0
e) 15x^2 **k)** -9x^2
f) 28x^3 **l)** -4x^{15}

Q2 a) 7a^6 **c)** 1
b) 50t^4 **d)** -4w^5

Q3 a) 5x^4 **f)** 21x^2 + 12x
b) 14x^6 **g)** 32x^7 + 2x
c) 1 **h)** 15x^4 + 3x^2 + 1
d) 4x + 1 **i)** 3x^8 + 5x^4 + 2x
e) 9x^8 + 3

Q4 36x^3 + 3x^2 + 8x + 6

Q5 15x^4 + 28x^3 + 24x^2 + 4x + 10

Q6 40x^7 + 24x^5 + 48x^3 + 14x

Q7 44d^3 + 36d^2 + 18d + 14

Q8 a) −12x^2 − 2x **d)** 6x^2 + 2x − 8
b) 15x^2 + 6x + 1 **e)** -1/x^2
c) −18x^2 − 4x **f)** −2/x^3

Q9 i) 1 **ii)** 1.75

Q10 a) −2, −2 **g)** −1.5, −6
b) 5, 44 **h)** 3, 12
c) −2, 4 **i)** 3, 0.75
d) 2, −4 **j)** −2, −0.5
e) −2, 4 **k)** 2, −0.25
f) 6, 24 **l)** −2, 0.25

Q11 dy/dx = 3x^2 + 6x + 1. Gradient at x = 2 is 3(2²) + (6×2) + 1 = 12 + 12 + 1 = 25. This is positive, so must be Graph B as Graphs A and C have negative gradients at x = 2.

Q12 (2, 14)

Q13 (0.5, 8)

Q14 a) Between 23 minutes and 2 hours 37 minutes = 2 hours 14 minutes.
b) v = −2t + 3
c) after 30 mins, v = 2 km/h, after 1 hour, v = 1 km/h

Q15 a) d = 2t^2(t + 1) = 2(6)²(6 + 1) = 2 × 36 × 7 = 504 metres
b) Velocity = d(d)/dt = 6t^2 + 4t
So after 6 seconds: Velocity = 6(6)² + 4(6) = 216 + 24 = 240 m/s
c) Acceleration = d(velocity)/dt = 12t + 4. So after 6 seconds acceleration = 12(6) + 4 = 76 m/s²

Q16 a) v = 4(40)² + 2(40) + 3
v = 6483 m/s
b) Acceleration = dv/dt = 8t + 2, so acceleration after 40 s is: 8(40) + 2 = 322 m/s²

Q17 a) dy/dx = 4x, so turning point is when 4x = 0, so x = 0. Turning point is (0, 0). Graph is y = ax^2 graph, a > 0, so turning point is a minimum.
b) dy/dx = 10x + 1, so turning point is when 10x + 1 = 0, so x = -0.1. Turning point is (-0.1, -0.05). Graph is y = ax^2 graph, a > 0, so turning point is a minimum.
c) dy/dx = 6x + 2, so turning point is when 6x + 2 = 0, so x = −1/3. Turning point is (−1/3, −5$\frac{1}{3}$). Graph is y = ax^2 graph, a > 0, so turning point is a minimum.
d) dy/dx = −2x + 4, so turning point is when −2x + 4 = 0, so x = 2. Turning point is (2, −4). Graph is y = ax^2 graph, a < 0, so turning point is a maximum.
e) y = x^2 − 4x − 32, so dy/dx = 2x − 4 Turning point is when 2x − 4 = 0, so x = 2. So turning point is (2, −36). Graph is y = ax^2 graph, a > 0, so turning point is a minimum.

Q18 a) 4x^3 − 2x − 3
b) 20x^4 + 36x^3
c) 2x^2 + $\frac{2}{x^3}$ + 10
d) 3x^2 + 15x − $\frac{12}{x^5}$

Q19 a) dy/dx = x^2 − 2x − 3
So turning points are when x^2 − 2x − 3 = (x + 1)(x − 3) = 0. So x = −1 and x = 3. So turning points are (−1, −6$\frac{1}{3}$) and (3, −17).
b) dy/dx = 4x^2 − 32x + 48
So turning points are when x^2 − 8x + 12 = (x − 2)(x − 6) = 0. So x = 2 and x = 6. So turning points are (2, 42$\frac{2}{3}$) and (6, 0).
c) dy/dx = 2x^2 − 9x − 5
So turning points are when 2x^2 − 9x − 5 = (2x + 1)(x − 5) = 0. So x = −0.5 and x = 5. So turning points are (−0.5, −$\frac{17}{24}$) and (5, −56$\frac{1}{6}$).
d) dy/dx = 3x^2 + 12x + 12
So turning points are when x^2 + 4x + 4 = (x + 2)(x + 2) = 0. So x = −2. So turning point is (−2, −7).

Q20 a) C = −20(0)³ + 40(0)² − 10 = −10 °C.
b) dC/dt = −60t^2 + 80t So dC/dt = −60(0.5)² + 80(0.5) = 25 °C.
c) dC/dt = 0, so −60t^2 + 80t = 0, Using the quadratic formula:
$$t = \frac{-b \pm \sqrt{b^2 - 4ac}}{2a}$$
$$t = \frac{-80 \pm \sqrt{80^2 - 4(-60)(0)}}{2(-60)}$$
so t = 0 and 1$\frac{1}{3}$
The heater was switched off after 1 hour 20 minutes.

Section Four — Geometry and Measure
Scale Drawings P.67

Q1 10 cm long and 7.5 cm wide
Q2 65 cm long and 17 cm wide
Q3 13 mm wide gap, 78 cm wide oven.
Q4 a) Room 4 cm long and 3 cm wide
b) Window 2 cm, door 0.75 cm
Q5 a) 3.3 cm **c)** 48.8 km
b) 13.2 km
Q6 a) 12.25 m **b)** 4.02 m²

Geometry P.68-P.69

Q1 a) x = 47° **b)** y = 154°
c) z = 22° **d)** p = 35°, q = 45°
Q2 a) a = 146°
b) m = 131°, z = 48°
c) x = 68°, p = 112°
d) s = 20°, t = 90°
Q3 a) x = 96°, p = 38°
b) a = 108°, b = 23°, c =95°
c) d = 120°, e = 60°, f = 60°, g = 120°
d) h = 155°, i = 77.5°, j = 102.5°, k = 77.5°
Q4 a) b = 70° c = 30°
d = 50° e = 60°
f = 150°
b) g = 21° h = 71°
i = 80° j = 38°
k = 92°
c) l = 35° m = 145°
n = 55° p = 125°

Answers: P.69 – P.74

Q5 a) $x = 162°$ $y = 18°$
b) $x = 87°$ $y = 93°$
$z = 93°$
c) $a = 30°$ $2a = 60°$
$5a = 150°$ $4a = 120°$

Q6 a) $a = 141°$, $b = 141°$, $c = 39°$,
$d = 141°$, $e = 39°$
b) $a = 47°$, $b = 47°$, $c = 133°$,
$d = 43°$ $e = 43°$
c) $m = 140°$, $n = 140°$, $p = 134°$,
$q = 46°$, $r = 40°$

Polygons P.70-P.71

Q1 Isosceles.

Q2

order of rotational symmetry = 6.

Q3 a) Angles at a point sum to 360°,
hence m + m + r = 360°.
Angles in a pentagon sum to 540°.
We know two angles are 90°, so we
are left with 360°. The only angles
left are m, m and r so
m + m + r must equal 360°.
b) r°.
c)

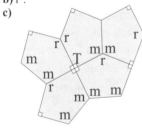

Q4 a) $90° + 60° = 150°$

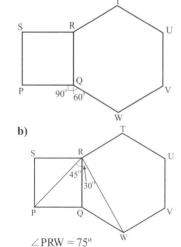

b)

∠PRW = 75°
c) 180 – (360/n) = 150
180n – 360 = 150n
30n = 360 ⇒ n = 12

Q5 540° – (100° + 104° + 120°)
= 216° for two equal angles
∴1 angle = 108°

Q6 a) Interior angle = 165°
b) Exterior angle = 180° – 165° = 15°
Sum of exterior angles = 15 × 24
= 360°

Q7 a) $\frac{360}{5} = 72°$
b) $\frac{180 - 72}{2} = 54°$
c) i) 90°   ii) 36°
d) Lines ST and BE are parallel, so
angle ABE = angle BAS = 36°
(alternate angles).
Triangle ABE is isosceles, so
angle BEA = angle ABE = 36°.

Q8 $(2n – 4)90 = 2520$, n = 16

Q9 a) $(\frac{360}{5}) ÷ 2 = 36°$
b) OX = 5 cos 36° = 4.045 cm.
Hence MX = 5 – 4.045 = 0.95 cm.

Q10 a)

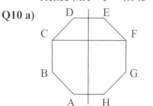

b) Angle CDE = angle DEF
$= \frac{(2 \times 8 - 4)90}{8} = 135$
so angle EFC $= \frac{360 - 2(135)}{2} = 45°$
OR exterior angle = 45° = angle
EFC (alternate angles).

Symmetry P.72

Q1 a) 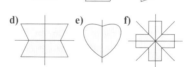 b)   c)

d)   e)   f)

Q2 a) 6   b) 8   c) 5   d) 3

Q3

1   2   1

Order of Rotation

1   1   2   2

Q4 a)

Order of
Rotation = 3

b)

Order of
Rotation = 1

c)

Order of
Rotation = 2

d)

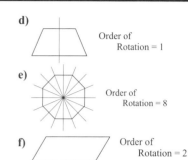

Order of
Rotation = 1

e)

Order of
Rotation = 8

f)

Order of
Rotation = 2

Circle Geometry P.73-P.75

Q1 BD bisects AC and meets it at an angle
of 90°, so BD must be a diameter of the
circle.
So BD = 2 × 9 = 18 m

Q2 a) BD = 5 cm (as the tangents BD and
CD are equal).
b) Angle COD = 70° (= 180° – (20° +
90°)), since the tangent CD meets
the radius OC at an angle of 90°.
c) Angle COB = 140° (since angle
BOD equals angle COD).

Q3 Both 90°

Q4 a) BAD = 80° (opposite angle C in
cyclic quadrilateral)
b) EAB = 180 – 80 – 30 = 70°

Q5 a) BOE = 106° (angle at centre)
b) ACE = 32° (angle in opposite
segment)

Q6 a) ACD = 70° (angle in opposite
segment)
b) BAD = 180 – (30 + 70) = 80°
(opposite angles of a cyclic
quadrilateral total 180°)

Q7 a) Angles in the same segment.
b) $3x + 40 = 6x – 50$
$90 = 3x$
$30 = x$
angle ABD = 3(30) + 40 = 130°

Q8 There are 2 ways of answering
this question.

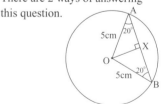

A diameter through O bisects the chord
at X so cos 20° = $\frac{AX}{5}$ ⟹
AX = 4.698 and
AB = 9.40 cm.
or by the sine rule $\frac{AB}{\sin 140°} = \frac{5}{\sin 20°}$
AB = $\frac{5 \sin 140°}{\sin 20°}$ = 9.40 cm

Q9 **a)** Angle ACB is an angle in a semicircle, so it is a right angle. So area of ABC = ½ × AC × BC = ½AC² = 64 cm²
By Pythagoras,
AB² = AC² + BC² = 2AC²
= 4(½AC²)
= 4 × 64 = 256
So AB = $\sqrt{256}$ = 16 cm

b) BX = 3AX and
BX + AX = 16 cm, so BX = 12 cm
and AX = 4 cm
AB and DE are intersecting chords, so AX × BX = DX × EX
12 × 4 = 6 × EX
EX = 48 ÷ 6 = 8 cm
So DE = 8 + 6 = 14 cm

Q10 **a)** Angle ABD = 70° (angle at centre = 2 × angle at circumference)
b) Angle ABC = 90° (angle in semicircle)
c) Angle DBC = 20° (90° – 70°)

Q11 **a)** 90° (angle in a semicircle)
b) The angle at A = 90° (tangent and radius are perpendicular).
The third angle in the triangle is 180 – 90 – 23 = 67° and so
x = 90 – 67 = 23°.
Or, by opposite segment theorem:
x = angle ABC = 23°.

Q12 **a)** With AD as a chord, angle ABD = ∠ACD = 30° (same segment); angle AXB = 85° (vertically opposite angles).
The third angles must be the same in both triangles so the triangles must be similar.
b) Ratio of lengths = $\frac{4}{8} = \frac{1}{2}$
so XB = 7.25 cm
c) angle BDC = 180 – 85 – 30 = 65°

Q13 **a)** 90° (angle in a semicircle)
b) Pythagoras is needed here:
AC² + 3² = 10²
AC² = 100 – 9 = 91
AC = 9.54 cm
c) AD = 5 cm so DC = 9.54 – 5 = 4.54 cm then Pythagoras gives
(4.54)² + 3² = (DOB)²
20.606 + 9 = (DOB)²
So DOB = 5.44 cm

Q14 **a)** Both angles are 90° (angle in a semicircle)
b) 3 × 6.5 = 5 × BX
So BX = 3.9 cm
c) 2.5 × (2.5 + 3 + 6.5) = 6 × YF
So YF = 5 cm

The Four Transformations P.76-P.77

Q1 **a), b), c)** — see diagram.

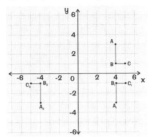

d) Rotation of +180° (or -180) about (0, 0)

Q2 **a), b), d), e)** — see diagram

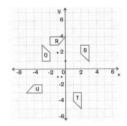

c) Rotation of +180° (or -180) about (0, 2).
f) 90° rotation anticlockwise about $\left(-\frac{1}{2}, -\frac{1}{2}\right)$.

Q3 **a)**

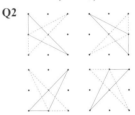

b) $\overrightarrow{QO} = \left(\begin{smallmatrix} -3 \\ -4 \end{smallmatrix}\right)$
$T = \left(\begin{smallmatrix} 11 \\ 8 \end{smallmatrix}\right) + \left(\begin{smallmatrix} -3 \\ -4 \end{smallmatrix}\right) = \left(\begin{smallmatrix} 8 \\ 4 \end{smallmatrix}\right)$
see diagram
c) $\left(\begin{smallmatrix} -1 \\ 2 \end{smallmatrix}\right) + \left(\begin{smallmatrix} 8 \\ 4 \end{smallmatrix}\right) + \left(\begin{smallmatrix} -3 \\ -4 \end{smallmatrix}\right) + \left(\begin{smallmatrix} -4 \\ -2 \end{smallmatrix}\right) = \left(\begin{smallmatrix} 0 \\ 0 \end{smallmatrix}\right)$

Q4 **a) to e)** — see diagram.

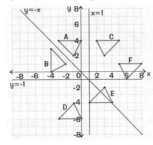

f) Rotation of +180° (or -180), centre (3, 0)

Q5 **a), b)** — see diagram.

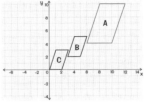

c) Ratio of areas C:A = 1:4

Congruence, Similarity and Enlargement P.78-P.79

Q1 **a)** Angle A shared. Parallel lines make corresponding angles equal so the triangles are similar.
b) Ratio of lengths given by
$\frac{AB}{AD} = \frac{12}{20} = \frac{3}{5}$
So $x = 25 \times \frac{3}{5} = 15$ cm

Also $\frac{y + 10}{y} = \frac{5}{3}$
$\Rightarrow 2y = 30, y = 15$ cm

Q2

Hence 7 ways to draw <u>another</u>.

Q3 **a)** Triangles APQ and STC (both isosceles and share either angle A or C)
b) Ratio AC:AQ = 24:7.5 = 3.2:1 so
AP = $15 \times \frac{1}{3.2}$ = 4.6875 cm
PT = 24 – 2 (4.6875) = 14.625 cm
c) Using $\frac{1}{2}$(base)(height)
= $\frac{1}{2}$(24)(9) = 108 cm²
d) Scale factor = $\frac{1}{3.2}$
Area scale factor = $\frac{1}{10.24}$
Area of triangle APQ
= $108 \times \frac{1}{10.24}$ = 10.5 cm²
e) 108 – 2 (10.5) = 87 cm²

Q4 **a) & b)**

c) triangle A₂B₂C₂
Q5 Widths in ratio 2:3, so volumes in ratio 8:27.
Volume = $30 \times \frac{27}{8}$ = 101 litres

Q6 **a)** All lengths must be enlarged in the same ratio for them to be similar.
b) 4 litres

14

Q7 **a)** 2 end faces 2 × (2 × 3) = 12 cm²
2 side faces 2 × (5 × 3) = 30 cm²
Top & bottom 2 × (5 × 2) = 20 cm²
Total = 62 cm²
b) SF for length = 1:4
SF for area = 1:16
new area = 62 × 16 = 992 cm²

Q8 **a)** volume = $\frac{1}{3}(\pi \times 100^2)(100)$
= 1047198 cm³ = 1.05 m³
b) 50 cm
c) ratio = 1:2³ = 1:8
d) Volume of small cone =
$1.05 \times \frac{1}{8}$ = 0.131 m³
e) volume of portion left =
1.05 – 0.131 = 0.919
so ratio = 0.919:0.131 = $\frac{0.919}{0.131}$:1
= 7:1

Perimeter and Area P.80-P.82

Q1 Area 24 cm², perimeter 20 cm

Q2 Area 25 cm², perimeter 20 cm

Q3 **a)** Area = (4 × 4) – (1 × 2 + ½ × π
×1²) + ½ × π × 2²
= 16 – 3.5708 + 6.2832
= 18.7 m² (1 d.p.)
b) Three 1 litre tins of paint are
needed for two coats.
c) Perimeter = 1 + 1 + (½ × π × 2)
+ 1 + 1 + 4 + (½ × π × 4) + 4
= 12 + 3π = 21.4 m (1 d.p.)

Q4 **a)** l = 24, w = 12, area = 288 m²
b) 1 Carpet tile = 0.50 × 0.50
=0.25 m²
So 288 m² ÷ 0.25 = 1152 tiles are
required.
c) £4.99 per m² => £4.99 for 4 tiles
Total cost = (1152 ÷ 4) × 4.99
= £1437.12

Q5 Area = 120 cm²

Q6 Each square = 0.6 m × 0.6 m
= 0.36 m².
Total area of material =
6 × 0.36 = 2.16 m²

Q7 Perimeter = 4 × $\sqrt{9000}$
= 379.47 m (2 d.p.)
Natasha ran: 11 × 379.47
= 4200 m (to nearest 100 m)

Q8 48 ÷ 5 = 9.6 m length. Area of
1 roll = 11 m × 0.5 m = 5.5 m².
48 m² ÷ 5.5 m² = $8\frac{8}{11}$ rolls of turf
required. Of course 9 should be
ordered.

Q9 Base length = 4773 ÷ 43 = 111 mm.

Q10 Area of metal blade = ½ × 35 ×
(70 + 155) = 3937.5 mm²

Q11 Area of larger triangle
= ½ × 14.4 × 10 = 72 cm².
Area of inner triangle = ½ × 5.76 × 4
= 11.52 cm².
Area of metal used for a bracket =
72 – 11.52 = 60.48 cm² so NO,
bracket is too heavy for the fixing.

Q12 T_1: ½ × 8 × 16 = 64 m²
Tr_1: ½ × 8 × (8 + 16) = 96 m²
Tr_2: ½ × 4 × (8 + 12) = 40 m²
T_2: ½ × 8 × 12 = 48 m²
Total area of glass sculpture = 248 m²

Q13 Area = ½ × 8.2 × 4.1 = 16.81 m²
Perimeter = 10.8 + 4.5 + 8.2
= 23.5 m.

Q14 **a)** Area of each isosceles triangle =
½ × 2.3 × 3.2 = 3.68 m²
b) Area of each side =
$(\sqrt{3.2^2 + 1.15^2}) \times 4$ = 13.6 m²
Groundsheet = 2.3 × 4 = 9.2 m²
c) Total material = 2 × 3.68 + 9.2 +
2 × 13.6 = 43.8 m²

Q15

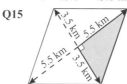

Area = ½ × product of diagonals
= ½ × 7 × 11 = 38.5 km².

Q16 B = major sector
C = chord
D = tangent

Q17 **a)** 117.607 m²
b) 45.216 = 45 m to 2 s.f.
c) 46.5 m to 1dp.
d) 14.152 cm² to 3dp.

Q18 **a)** Area = area of a full circle radius
10 cm. A = πr^2 = 3.14 × 10²
= 314 cm².
Circumference = π × D
= 3.14 × 20 = 62.8 cm.
Perimeter = 62.8 + 20 = 82.8 cm
b) Area = (area of a full circle radius
15 cm) + (area of a rectangle 15 ×
30 cm) = (π × 15²) + (15 × 30)
= 1156.5 cm².
Perimeter = (Circumference of a
full circle radius 15 cm) + 15 +15
(two shorter sides of rectangle) =
(π × 30) + 30 = 124.2 cm.
c) Area = Outer semi circle – Inner
semi circle = 510.25 m².
Perimeter = ½ Circumference of
larger + ½ Circumference of inner
+ 5 + 5 = ½ × π × 70 + ½ × π × 60
+ 10 = 214.1 m.

Q19 **a)** ABDC = $\frac{60}{360} \times \pi(30)^2 - \frac{60}{360} \times$
$\pi(20)^2$
= 261.8 mm²
b) 2(½π5²) = 78.5 mm².
Hence 261.8 + 78.5 = 340.3 mm².

Q20 **a)** 80/360 × π5² = 17.45 cm²
b) Area of triangle AOB =
$\frac{1}{2} \times 5 \times 5 \times \sin80°$ = 12.31 cm²
Shaded Area = 17.45 – 12.31
= 5.14 cm²

Surface Area P.83-P.84

Q1 **a) - c)**

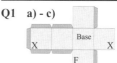

Q2

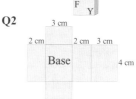

Other arrangements are possible.

Q3 **a)** H, F and D
b) Line symmetry through lines
AF, DH, BG and CE. Rotational
symmetry of order 4.
c) 5 faces and vertices, 8 edges.

Q4 **a)** I
b) 64 cm²
c) 64 × 6 = 384 cm²
d)

Q5 Net B

Q6 No, Hannah would need more than
603 cm².

Q7 Surface area = 4 × π × 3²
= 113.10 cm² (to 2 d.p)

Q8 Surface area of cone = $\pi r l + \pi r^2$
= (π × 1.5 × 8) + (π × 1.5²)
= 44.77 cm² (to 2 d.p)
Height of triangular prism = $\sqrt{3^2 - 1.5^2}$
= $\sqrt{6.75}$ = 2.598... cm
Surface area of triangular prism =
$2(\frac{1}{2} \times 3 \times 2.598...) + 3(3 \times 8)$
= 79.79 cm² (to 2 d.p.)
Therefore the triangular prism has the
largest surface area.

Q9 Surface area of hemisphere =
$\pi r^2 + \frac{1}{2}(4\pi r^2)$
$75\pi = 3\pi r^2$
$r^2 = 25$, radius = 5 cm

Q10 AB² = 2² + 1.5² AB = 2.5 m
1 panel on roof = ½AB × $\frac{5}{2}$
= 1.25 × 2.5 = 3.125 m²
Front of greenhouse = (2.5 × 4) +
(½ × 4 × 1.5) = 13 m²
Total = 3.125 + 13 = 16.125 m²

Volume P.85-P.87

Q1 a) $\frac{1}{2}\pi(0.35)^2 = 0.192$ m^2
b) $0.1924 \times 3 = 0.577$ m^3

Q2 a) $\pi(2.5^2 - 2^2) = 7.07$ m^2
£16 × 7.07 = £113.12 = £110 to nearest £10.
b) Volume = $\pi(2)^2 \times 0.50 = 6.28$ m^3 so use 6.28 × 15 = 94 ml treatment to the nearest ml.

Q3 a) Volume Cube = Volume Cylinder
$10^3 = \pi r^2 \times 10$ so $r^2 = \frac{10^2}{\pi}$, $r = 5.64$ cm
b) S.A. of cylinder = $2\pi rh + 2\pi r^2 =$ $2\pi \times 5.64... \times 10 + 2\pi \times (5.64...)^2$ = 554.49 cm^2

Q4 a) $\pi(5)^2(16) = 1257$ cm^3
b) $\pi(5)^2 h = 600$
$h = \frac{600}{25\pi} = 7.64$ cm

Q5 $(3)(3)(0.5) - \pi(0.7)^2(0.5) = 3.73$ cm^3

Q6 Volume = $\frac{1}{3} \times (230 \times 230) \times 139$ = 2 451 033 m^3

Q7 $(\pi \times (2)^2 \times 110) +$ $(\frac{1}{2}(14 + 20) \times 6 \times 20) = 3422.30$ cm^3 $2 \times 3422.30 = 6844.60$ cm^3 = 6.84 l

Q8 a) $(60)(30) + (30)(120) = 5400$ cm^2
b) $5400 \times 100 = 540000$ cm^3 = 0.54 m^3

Q9 Volume = $\frac{4}{3}\pi r^3 = \frac{4}{3} \times \pi \times 15^3$ = 14137 cm^3

Q10 $\frac{\text{volume of cylinder}}{\text{volume of hemisphere}} = \frac{\pi r^2 h}{\frac{1}{2} \times \frac{4}{3}\pi r^3}$
$= \frac{6\pi r^2 h}{4\pi r^3} = \frac{3h}{2r}$
$\frac{3h}{2r} = 3 \Rightarrow h = 2r$

Q11 a) $\frac{1}{2}(\frac{4}{3}\pi(1.3)^3) + \pi(1.3)^2 \times 1.8$ $+ \frac{1}{3}\pi(1.3)^2 \times 1.2 = 16.28$ cm^3
b) Volume of sand in hemisphere and cone parts remain the same so change is in cylindrical part. Therefore $h + 0.3 = 1.8$, $h = 1.5$ cm.
c) Volume of sand transferred = $\frac{1}{2}(\frac{4}{3}\pi(1.3)^3) + \pi(1.3)^2 \times 1.5$ = 12.57 cm^3
Time Taken = $\frac{12.57}{0.05} \approx 251$ secs. = 4 minutes 11 secs

Q12 a) Volume of ice cream
$= \frac{1}{3}\pi(R^2H - r^2h) + \frac{1}{2}(\frac{4}{3}\pi R^3)$
$= \frac{1}{3}\pi(2.5^2 \times 10 - 1^2 \times 4)$
$+ \frac{1}{2}(\frac{4}{3}\pi \times 2.5^3)$
= 93.99 cm^3 of ice cream.

b) Outer surface area of cone = πRl
Using Pythagoras,
$l^2 = 10^2 + 2.5^2 = 106.25$,
$l = 10.3$ cm. So S.A. = $\pi \times 2.5 \times 10.3 = 81.0$ cm^2

Q13 Vol. increase is a cylinder of height 4.5 cm. So vol. increase = $\pi(5)^2 \times 4.5 = 353.4$ cm^3.
Volume of each marble = $\frac{353.4}{200}$ = 1.767 cm^3
$\frac{4}{3}\pi r^3 = 1.767 \Rightarrow r = 0.75$ cm

Q14 a) $x(3-x)(5-x)$ m^3 or $x^3 - 8x^2 + 15x$
b)
X	0	1	2	3
V	0	8	6	0
c)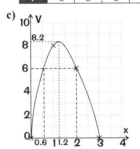
d) about 8.2 m^3
e) ends $\quad$ 2(1.2)(1.8) = $\quad$ 4.32 +
side faces 2(1.2)(3.8) = $\quad$ 9.12 +
tops $\quad$ 2(3.8)(1.8) = $\quad$ 13.68
So area is about $\quad$ 27.12 m^2
f) $x = 2$ or $x = 0.6$
If $x = 0.6$:
ends $\quad$ 2(0.6)(2.4) = $\quad$ 2.88 +
side faces 2(0.6)(4.4) = $\quad$ 5.28 +
tops $\quad$ 2(2.4)(4.4) = $\quad$ 21.12
$\quad$ 29.28 m^2
If $x = 2$:
ends $\quad$ 2(2)(1) = $\quad$ 4 +
side faces 2(2)(3) = $\quad$ 12 +
tops $\quad$ 2(1)(3) = $\quad$ 6
$\quad$ 22 m^2
Maximum Total S.A. ≈ 29.28 m^2

Time P.88

Q1 a) 5 am $\quad$ d) 3.58 pm
b) 2.48 pm $\quad$ e) 10.30 pm
c) 3.16 am $\quad$ f) 12.01 am

Q2 a) 2330 $\quad$ d) 1215
b) 1022 $\quad$ e) 0830
c) 0015 $\quad$ f) 1645

Q3 145 mins

Q4 a) 8 hours $\quad$ c) 11 hrs 56 mins
b) 10 hours $\quad$ d) 47 hrs 48 mins

Q5 a) 3 hrs 15 mins $\quad$ c) 7 hrs 18 mins
b) 24 mins $\quad$ d) 1 hr 12 mins

Q6 a) 2.33 hrs $\quad$ b) 3.1 hrs $\quad$ c) 0.33 hrs

Q7 a) Train 3 $\quad$ b) Train 1 $\quad$ c) 1208

Speed, Distance and Time P.89-P.90

Q1 60 km/h
Q2 165 km
Q3 2 hrs 40 mins
Q4
Distance Travelled	Time Taken	Average Speed
210 km	3 hrs	70 km/h
135 km	4 hrs 30 mins	30 km/h
105 km	2 hrs 30 mins	42 km/h
9 km	45 mins	12 km/h
640 km	48 mins	800 km/h
70 km	1 hr 10 mins	60 km/h

Q5 a) 9.1 m/s $\quad$ b) 32.7 km/h
Q6 540 km/h
Q7 Journey takes 3 hrs 39 mins.
07.05 to 10.30 is 3 hrs 25 mins.
So Pete will not be in London on time.
Q8 a) 98.9 km/h $\quad$ c) 99.2 km/h
b) 72.56 s
Q9 a) 5 hrs 31 mins 30 s $\quad$ c) 73.3 km/h
b) 405 km
Q10 He should set off no later than 2.15 pm.
Q11 a) 2 hrs 14 mins $\quad$ c) 1346 and 1401
b) 1 hr 59 mins
Q12 16 km/h is faster. 38 and 42 mins.
Q13 a) 488 km $\quad$ b) 921 km $\quad$ c) 497 km/h
Q14 a) 8.1 m/s $\quad$ b) 7.4 m/s
Q15 a) 220 km
b) 5 mins 4 s (to the nearest second)
Q16 1 hr 27 mins
Q17 a) 4.8 m/s $\quad$ c) 14.4 m/s
b) 14.4 m/s $\quad$ d) 17.3 km/h, 51.8 km/h
Q18 122.7 s, 124.2 s and 127.7 s

D/T and S/T Graphs P.91-P.92

Q1 a) 4 km
b) 15 mins and 45 mins
c) 2.4 km/h
d) 1100
e) 10 km/h
f) 1030
Q2 a) 1 hr 25 mins
b) 1 hr 15 mins
c) 25.4 km/h
d) 86.4 km/h
e) No. Can't get to Ingleton and back.
Q3 a) A 80.0 km/h, fastest.
B 57.1 km/h
C 66.7 km/h
D 44.4 km/h
E 50.0 km/h
b) steepest slope was fastest, least steep slope was slowest.

16

Q4

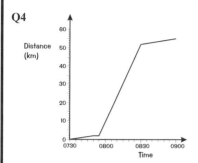

He waited for 5 mins.

Q5 a) 3 hours
b) 4 to 6 hours into the journey
c) Travelling at a constant speed of 15 km/h

Q6 a) acceleration
= change in speed ÷ time
= (100 − 60)/1 = 40 km/h²
b) The first hour.

Q7 a)

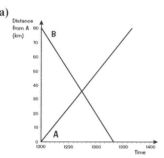

b) accept 1243-1245
c) accept 35-36 km

Q8 a)

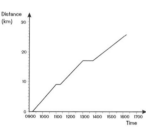

b) 25.75 km   c) 3.68 km/h
d) Her fastest speed was in the first section (steepest graph) — her speed was 5.14 km/h.

Unit Conversion P.93

Q1 a) 200 cm   i) 6000 mm
b) 33 mm   j) 2000 kg
c) 4000 g   k) 3 kg
d) 0.6 kg   l) 86 mm
e) 0.65 km   m) 0.55 tonnes
f) 9000 g   n) 354 cm
g) 0.007 kg   o) 7 mm
h) 0.95 kg   p) 4.2 l

Q2 a) 0.47 m   b) 470 mm

Q3 a) 300 cm   c) 0.003 km
b) 3000 mm

Q4 a) 0.2 km   c) 7 km
b) 2 km   d) 0.02 km²

Q5 a) 167 cm   c) 0.11 cm²
b) 33.3 cm   d) 0.056 cm²

Q6 a) £4.69   b) £51.07

Conversion Graphs P.94

Q1 a) i) £5   ii) £9.50   iii) £17
b) No (each 4.5-km journey costs more than £8)

Q2 a) $4.50   c) £2
b) $2.25   d) £3.65 (+/- £0.05)

Q3 a) i) 12-13 miles
ii) 43-44 miles
iii) 56-57 miles
b) i) 63-65 km
ii) 15-17 km
iii) 47-49 km

Constructions P.95

Q1

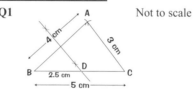

Not to scale

Q2

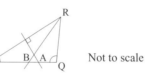

Not to scale
Length BA = 0.87 cm

Q3

Not to scale

Q4

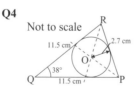

Not to scale
Radius of the circle = 2.7 cm

Bearings P.96

Q1 a) 245°   b) 310°
c) 035°   d) 131°
e) 297°, 028°, 208°

Q2 a)

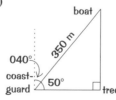

i) 268 m
ii) 225 m
b) 350² = 122 500.
225² + 268² = 122 449

Q3

a) 96 km
b) 255 km
c) 266 km
d) 156°
e) 082°
f) 177°

Q4

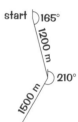

2500 m, 010°

Section Five — Pythagoras and Trigonometry
Pythagoras' Theorem P.97-P.99

Q1 a) 10.8 cm   f) 7.89 m
b) 6.10 m   g) 9.60 cm
c) 5 cm   h) 4.97 cm
d) 27.0 mm   i) 6.80 cm
e) 8.49 m   j) 8.5 cm

Q2 a = 3.32 cm   f = 8.62 m
b = 6 cm   g = 6.42 m
c = 6.26 m   h = 19.2 mm
d = 5.6 mm   i = 9.65 m
e = 7.08 mm   j = 48.7 mm

Q3 k = 6.55 cm   q = 7.07 cm
l = 4.87 m   r = 7.50 m
m = 6.01 m   s = 9.45 mm
n = 12.4 cm   t = 4.33 cm
p = 5.22 cm   u = 7.14 m

Q4 9.7 m

Q5 a) 12 cm, 7.94 cm
b) 40.9 cm
c) 89.7 cm²

Q6 314 m

Q7 91.9 cm

Q8 5.0 m

Q9 4.58 m

Q10 AB: 5 (don't need Pythagoras)

CD: $\sqrt{10}$ = 3.16

EF: $\sqrt{13}$ = 3.61

GH: $\sqrt{8}$ = 2.83

JK: $\sqrt{5}$ = 2.24

LM: $\sqrt{26}$ = 5.10

PQ: $\sqrt{20}$ = 4.47

RS: $\sqrt{45}$ = 6.71

TU: $\sqrt{13}$ = 3.61

Q11 a) 5

b) $\sqrt{17}$ = 4.12

c) 5

d) $\sqrt{58}$ = 7.62

e) $\sqrt{26}$ = 5.10

f) parallelogram

Q12 a) $\sqrt{41}$ = 6.40

b) $\sqrt{98}$ = 9.90

c) $\sqrt{53}$ = 7.28

d) $\sqrt{34}$ = 5.83

e) 4 (don't need Pythagoras here)

f) $\sqrt{37}$ = 6.08

Q13 a) $\sqrt{10}$ = 3.16

b) $\sqrt{130}$ = 11.40

c) $\sqrt{8}$ = 2.83

d) $\sqrt{233}$ = 15.26

e) $\sqrt{353}$ = 18.79

f) $\sqrt{100}$ = 10

Q14 192 km

Q15

13.9 km from the starting point.
150° to return to base.

Trigonometry — Sin, Cos, Tan
P.100-P.102

		(tan)	(sin)	(cos)
Q1	**a)**	0.306	0.292	0.956
	b)	8.14	0.993	0.122
	c)	0.0875	0.0872	0.996
	d)	0.532	0.469	0.883
	e)	1	0.707	0.707

Q2 a = 1.40 cm   c = 5.31 cm

b = 6 cm   d = 10.8 cm

θ = 28.1°

Q3 e = 12.6 cm   g = 6.71 m

f = 11.3 cm   h = 30.1 cm

θ = 49.5°

Q4 i = 4.89 cm   k = 5.32 cm

j = 3.79 cm   l = 41.6 cm

θ = 52.4°

Q5 m = 11.3 cm   t = 59.8 cm

n = 18.8 cm   u = 14.5 cm

p = 8.62 cm   v = 11.7 cm

q = 21.3 cm   w = 11.7 cm

r = 54.6°

Q6 a)

30   40   50   hypotenuse

b) 36.9°

Q7 a)

P (1,2)   3   Q (4,2)   5.83   5   R (4,-3)

b) 59.0°

c) 31.0°

Q8 a)

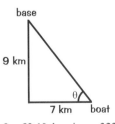

b) 71.6°

c) 36.9°

d) 71.5°

Q9 2.1 m

Q10 62°

Q11 20.5°

Q12

base   9 km   7 km   θ   boat

θ = 52.1°, bearing = 322°

Q13 a) both 30.8 cm

b) 27.5 cm   **c)** 385 cm²

Q14

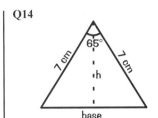

height = 5.90, base = 7.52,
so area = 22.2 cm².

Q15 a) 8.23 cm

b) 4.75 cm   **c)** 39.1 cm²

Q16 a) 10.8 cm

b) 150.8 cm²   **c)** 21.0°

Q17

16°   ?   1020 m   1235 m   750 m

Q18

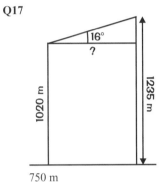

Q19

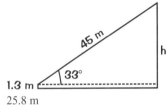

a) 102.4 m, 69.5 m

b) 32.9 m

Q20

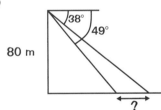

86.6 km

18

The Sine and Cosine Rules
P.103-P.104

Q1 $a = 4.80$ cm $f = 5.26$ cm
$b = 25.8$ mm $g = 9.96$ cm
$c = 13.0$ cm $h = 20.2$ mm
$d = 8.89$ m $i = 3.72$ m
$e = 18.4$ cm $j = 8.29$ cm

Q2 $k = 51°$ $r = 64°$
$l = 46°$ $s = 18°$
$m = 43°$ $t = 49°$
$p = 45°$ $u = 88°$
$q = 36°$

Q3 $a = 63°$ $i = 5.0$ mm
$b = 45°$ $j = 68°$
$c = 8.9$ cm $k = 203$ mm
$d = 27°$ $l = 127$ mm
$e = 10.5$ cm $m = 24.1$ cm
$g = 49°$ $n = 149°$
$h = 78°$ $p = 16°$

Q4 **a)** 46°
b) 52°   **c)** 82°

Q5 12.0 m

Q6 **a)** 28.8 km   **b)** 295.5°

Q7

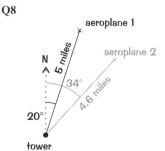

Diagonals 11.2 cm and 6.6 cm.

Q8

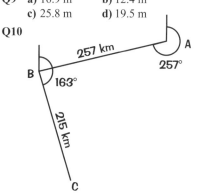

Distance = 1.2 miles.
The alarm should be ringing because the planes are less than 3 miles apart, so the software seems reliable.

Q9 **a)** 16.9 m   **b)** 12.4 m
c) 25.8 m   **d)** 19.5 m

Q10

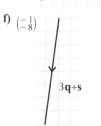

a) 86°
b) 323 km
c) 215°

Q11 a)

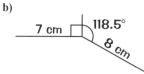

7.1 cm

b)

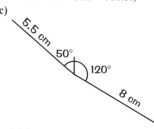

14.5 cm
(118.5° comes from the fact that the minute hand is at 19.75 mins.
$19.75 ÷ 60 × 360 = 118.5$.)

c)

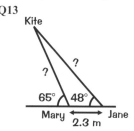

13.5 cm

Q12 Height of building = 35 m

Q13
Kite

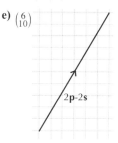

Mary's string = 5.85 m
Jane's string = 7.13 m

3D Pythagoras and Trigonometry
P.105

Q1 **a)** 59.0°   **c)** 25 cm
b) 23.3 cm   **d)** 21.1°

Q2 **a)** 42.5 cm   **b)** 50.9 cm

Q3 **a)** 36.1 cm, 21.5 cm, 31.0 cm
b) 36.9 cm

Q4 **a)** 15.4 cm   **b)** 20.4 cm

Q5 The 85p box

Q6 **a)** 3.82 cm
b) 45.8 cm^2
c) 137.5 cm^3

Sin, Cos and Tan for Larger Angles P.106

Q1 $a = 5.7$ cm $e = 13.0$ cm
$B = 38.9°$ $F = 62.6°$
$c = 8.2$ cm $G = 115.4°$
$D = 140°$

Q2 **a)** 122.9°   **c)** 135°
b) 170.0°   **d)** 94.0°

Q3 32.1 m

Q4 **a)** 109°
b) Front = 28.5 m, roof = 107.6 m
c) 24.2 m

Q5 24.6 km

Q6 42.5° and 137.5°

Q7 153.5°

Vectors P.107-P.108

Q1 **a)**

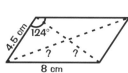

b) i) $\binom{-1}{-4}$ **ii)** $\binom{4}{0}$ **iii)** $\binom{5}{4}$
c) Isosceles

Q2 **a)**

b) Using Pythagoras,
$|\vec{AC}| = \sqrt{4^2 + 3^2} = 5$

Q3 **a)** $\binom{2}{1}$ **p+q**

b) $\binom{2}{5}$

p-q

c) $\binom{6}{-2}$ 2**r**

d) $\binom{1}{1}$ **s+p**

e) $\binom{6}{10}$

2**p-2s**

f) $\binom{-1}{-8}$

3**q+s**

g) $\binom{6}{0}$

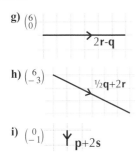

$\longrightarrow$ 2r-q

h) $\binom{6}{-3}$

$\frac{1}{2}$q+2r

i) $\binom{0}{-1}$

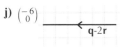

$\downarrow$ p+2s

j) $\binom{-6}{0}$

$\longleftarrow$ q-2r

Q4 a) 1   f) 5
     b) 3.61   g) 8.60
     c) 1   h) 8.49
     d) 3.61   i) 9.43
     e) 6.08   j) 11.18

Q5 a) $\binom{3}{3}$ d) 5.39

     b) 4.24   e) $\binom{2}{-2}$

     c) $\binom{5}{-2}$ f) 2.83

Q6 a) $2y$ d) $2y + 2x$
     b) $y + x$ e) $4y + 2x$
     c) $-y - x$ f) $2x$

Q7 a) i) $\overrightarrow{ED}$ or $\overrightarrow{AF}$ v) $\overrightarrow{BE}$
     ii) $\overrightarrow{EF}$ or $\overrightarrow{DC}$ vi) $\overrightarrow{AC}$
     iii) $\overrightarrow{AE}$ vii) $\overrightarrow{EC}$ or $\overrightarrow{AB}$
     iv) $\overrightarrow{BA}$ viii) $\overrightarrow{EB}$
     b) i) 48 cm²   ii) 60 cm²

Q8 a) i) $2a$ ii) $b - 2a$ iii) $a - b$
     b) $\overrightarrow{AC} = -2b + 2a = 2(a - b)$.
     Since $\overrightarrow{AC}$ is a multiple of $\overrightarrow{PQ}$, they
     must both be in the same direction
     and therefore parallel.

Section Six — Statistics and Probability
Mean, Median, Mode and Range P.109-P.110

Q1 3 tries

Q2 mean = 1.333 (to 3 dp)
     median = 1.5
     mode = 2
     range = 11

Q3 a) mean = £12,944, or £13,000 to the
     nearest £500
     median = £12,000
     mode = £7,500
     b) mode
     c) E.g. mean — they should use the
     highest value to attract people to
     the job.

Q4 a) 0 minutes   b) 0 minutes
     c) 0 minutes
     d) No, according to the raw data.

Q5 73.5 kg

Q6 20 kg

Q7 97%

Q8 a) 22   b) 74

Q9 a) 3.5   b) 3.5   c) 5

Q10 a) Both spend a mean of 2 hours.
     b) The range for Jim is 3 hours and
     for Bob is 2 hours.
     c) The amount of TV that Jim
     watches each night is more variable
     than the amount that Bob watches.

Q11 a) 1 day
     b) 2 days
     c) The statement is true according to
     the data.

Q12 a) mode
     b) median   c) mean

Quartiles and Comparing Distributions P.111

Q1 a) 65 g   b) The 2nd quartile (or Q_2)

Q2 a) $1020 - 80 = 940$
     b) 510   c) 700   d) 840

Q3 200

Q4 a) 325   b) 50

Q5 Mean (before)
         = 3·61 fillings per child
     Mean (after)
         = 2·08 fillings per child
     Mode (before)
         = 4 fillings per child
     Mode (after)
         = 2 fillings per child
     (all other things being equal, I'd say
     that the dental hygienist has decreased
     the number of fillings received by
     each child.)

Frequency Tables – Finding Averages P.112-P.113

Q1 a) 12   b) 12   c) 2

Q2 a)

Subject	M	E	F	A	S
Frequency	5	7	3	4	6

     b) 36 French lessons   c) English

Q3

Length (m)	4 and under	6	8	10	12	14 and over
Frequency	3	5	6	4	1	1

     a) 8 m   b) 8 m   c) 14 m

Q4

Weight (kg)	Frequency	Weight × Frequency
51	40	2040
52	30	1560
53	45	2385
54	10	540
55	5	275

     a) 52 kg   b) 2 kg
     c) 53 kg
     d) 52 kg (to nearest kg)

Q5 mean = 3.75
     mode = 3
     median = 4

Q6 a) 4   b) 3   c) 3.2 (to 1 dp)

Q7 a) i) False, mode is 8.
     ii) False, they are equal.
     iii) True
     b) iv)

Grouped Frequency Tables P.114

Q1 a)

Speed (km/h)	$40 \leq s < 45$	$45 \leq s < 50$	$50 \leq s < 55$	$55 \leq s < 60$	$60 \leq s < 65$
Frequency	4	8	10	7	3
Mid-Interval	42.5	47.5	52.5	57.5	62.5
Frequency × Mid-Interval	170	380	525	402.5	187.5

     Estimated mean = 52 km/h
     (to nearest km/h)
     b) 22 skiers   c) 20 skiers

Q2 a)

Weight (kg)	Tally	Frequency	Mid-Interval	Frequency × Mid-Interval
$200 \leq w < 250$	IIII	4	225	900
$250 \leq w < 300$	ЖИ	5	275	1375
$300 \leq w < 350$	ЖИ II	7	325	2275
$350 \leq w < 400$	II	2	375	750

     b) 294 kg (to nearest kg)
     c) $300 \leq w < 350$ kg

Q3 a)

Number	$0 \leq n < 0.2$	$0.2 \leq n < 0.4$	$0.4 \leq n < 0.6$	$0.6 \leq n < 0.8$	$0.8 \leq n < 1$
Tally	ЖИ ЖИ II	ЖИ I	ЖИ ЖИ II	ЖИ ЖИ	ЖИ III
Frequency	12	6	12	10	8
Mid-Interval	0.1	0.3	0.5	0.7	0.9
Frequency × Mid-Interval	1.2	1.8	6	7	7.2

     b) $0 \leq n < 0.2$ and $0.4 \leq n < 0.6$
     c) $0.4 \leq n < 0.6$
     d) 0.483 (3 dp)

Cumulative Frequency P.115-P.116

Q1 accept:
     a) 133-134   c) 136-137
     b) 127-128   d) 8-10

Q2 a)

Number of passengers	$0 \leq n < 50$	$50 \leq n < 100$	$100 \leq n < 150$	$150 \leq n < 200$	$200 \leq n < 250$	$250 \leq n < 300$
Frequency	2	7	10	5	3	1
Cumulative Frequency	2	9	19	24	27	28
Mid-Interval	25	75	125	175	225	275
Frequency × Mid-Interval	50	525	1250	875	675	275

     Estimated mean = 130 passengers
     (to nearest whole number)

Answers: P.115 – P.118

b)

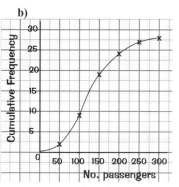

accept median of 118-122
passengers

c) $100 \leqslant n < 150$

Q3 a)

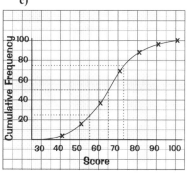

	0≤m<20	20≤m<40	40≤m<60	60≤m<80	80≤m<100
Mark (%)					
Frequency	2	12	18	5	3
Cumulative Frequency	2	14	32	37	40

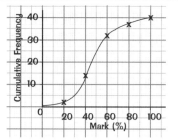

b) 36%-38%
c) 19%-21%
d) 45%-47%

Q4

Score	31≤s<41	41≤s<51	51≤s<61	61≤s<71	71≤s<81	81≤s<91	91≤s<101
Frequency	4	12	21	32	19	8	4
Cumulative frequency	4	16	37	69	88	96	100

a) $61 \leqslant s < 71$
b) $61 \leqslant s < 71$
c)

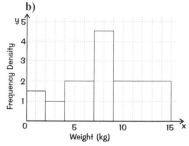

median = 65 (accept 64-66)
d) 73 – 55 = 18 (accept 17-19)

Q5 a)

Life (hours)	Frequency	Cumulative Frequency
900 ≤ L < 1000	10	10
1000 ≤ L < 1100	12	22
1100 ≤ L < 1200	15	37
1200 ≤ L < 1300	18	55
1300 ≤ L < 1400	22	77
1400 ≤ L < 1500	17	94
1500 ≤ L < 1600	14	108
1600 ≤ L < 1700	9	117

b) $1300 \leqslant L < 1400$

c)

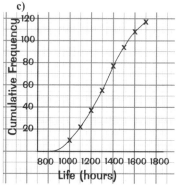

median = 1320 hours (±20)
d) lower quartile = 1150 (±20)
upper quartile = 1460 (±20)

Q6 a)

Time	2:00≤t<2:30	2:30≤t<3:00	3:00≤t<3:30	3:30≤t<4:00	4:00≤t<4:30
Tally	I	IIII	IIIIIIIIIII	IIIIII	III
Frequency	1	5	14	7	3
Cumulative frequency	1	6	20	27	30

b)

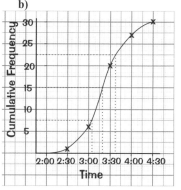

c) median = 3:19 (±3)
upper quartile = 3:37 (±3)
lower quartile = 3:05 (±3)
d) 0:32 (±5)

Histograms and Frequency Density
P.117-P.118

Q1 $4 \times 10 = 40$ people

Q2

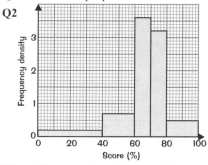

Q3 a) Frequency for $150 < x \leqslant 200 =$ 275

b)

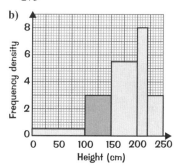

Q4 a)

Weight (kg)	0≤w<2	2≤w<4	4≤w<7	7≤w<9	9≤w<15
Frequency	3	2	6	9	12
Frequency density	1.5	1	2	4.5	2

b)

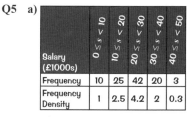

c) 23 hives

Q5 a)

Salary (£1000s)	0 ≤ s < 10	10 ≤ s < 20	20 ≤ s < 30	30 ≤ s < 40	40 ≤ s < 50
Frequency	10	25	42	20	3
Frequency Density	1	2.5	4.2	2	0.3

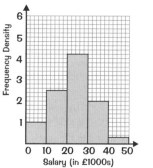

b) E.g. there are more people with higher salaries now than 10 years ago.

Q6 a)

Milk (litres)	Frequency	Frequency density	Mid-interval	Frequency × mid-interval
0≤C<1	6	6	0.5	3
1≤C<5	6	1.5	3	18
5≤C<8	6	2	6.5	39
8≤C<10	6	3	9	54
10≤C<15	6	1.2	12.5	75
15≤C<20	6	1.2	17.5	105

b) 8.2 litres (to 1 d.p.)

c)

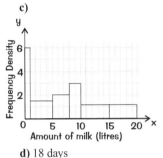

d) 18 days

Other Graphs and Charts P.119-P.120

Q1 $\frac{360°}{100}$ = 3.6° per gram

Carbohydrate	3.6 × 35 = 126°
Protein	3.6 × 15 = 54°
Fat	3.6 × 10 = 36°
Magical Fairy Dust	3.6 × 40 = 144°
	360°

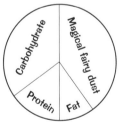

Q2 Sherrington 380,000 = 148° (approx)
2600 visitors = 1°
So, to the nearest 10,000:
Brompton = 2600 × 118° ≈ 310,000
Barny = 2600 × 44° ≈ 110,000
Livsea = 2600 × 50° ≈ 130,000

Q3 c)

Q4 It's not possible to tell whether more people voted for the Green Party in 2009, because you can't tell how many people voted in either election.

Q5 a) 60   b) 8   c) 4
d) e.g. Cola was the most popular and milk the least popular / cola was much more popular than milk.

Q6 a) Monday, Wednesday and Thursday.
b) Monday

Q7 a) About 60%   b) About 50%
c) On average, women live longer than men / husbands are usually older than wives. So, women in their 90s are far more likely to have lost their husbands than men in their 90s are to have lost their wives.

Probability P.121-P.124

Q1 a) 1/2   c) 1/6
b) 2/3   d) 0
And so should be arranged approximately like this on the number line.

Guatemalan stamp

Head on a coin

0   Five on a dice   0.5   Red ball   1

Q2 Debbie's chance of winning would be 1/9. This is greater than 0.1, so she would choose to play.

Q3 The probability of a head is still 1/2

Q4 1 − 0.27 = 0.73 or 73/100

Q5 a) 5/12   c) 3/12 = 1/4
b) 4/12 = 1/3   d) 9/12 = 3/4

Q6 a) 40/132 = 10/33
b) P(car being blue or green) = 45/132
P(not blue or green) = 87/132 = 29/44

Q7

	1	2	3	4	5
1	1,1	1,2	1,3	1,4	1,5
2	2,1	2,2	2,3	2,4	2,5
3	3,1	3,2	3,3	3,4	3,5
4	4,1	4,2	4,3	4,4	4,5
5	5,1	5,2	5,3	5,4	5,5
6	6,1	6,2	6,3	6,4	6,5

Q8 a)

Outcome	Frequency
W	8
D	5
L	7

b) The 3 outcomes are not equally likely.
c) 1/4
d) They are most likely to win.

Q9 a) $\frac{1}{13}$ b) $\frac{2}{39}$ c) $\frac{1}{36}$

Q10 a) $\frac{7}{12}$ b) $\frac{7}{12}$
c) The two events can both happen at the same time, since 3 is a white.

Q11 a) $\frac{2}{5}$ b) $\frac{4}{15}$ c) $\frac{2}{3}$

Q12 a) (1,1), (1,2), (1,3), (1,4), (1,5), (1,6), (1,7), (2,1), (2,2), (2,3), (2,4), (2,5), (2,6), (2,7), (3,1), (3,2), (3,3), (3,4), (3,5), (3,6), (3,7)

b)

	1	2	3	4	5	6	7
1	2	3	4	5	6	7	8
2	3	4	5	6	7	8	9
3	4	5	6	7	8	9	10

c) $\frac{1}{7}$ d) $\frac{11}{21}$
e) $\frac{2}{7}$ f) $\frac{5}{7}$
g) Subtract the answer to part e) from 1.

Q13 a)

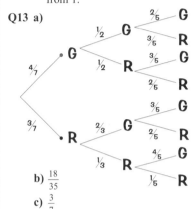

b) $\frac{18}{35}$
c) $\frac{3}{7}$

Q14 a) 14/40 or 0.35
b) 24/60 = 0.4
c) 38/100 = 0.38

Q15 4 times

Q16

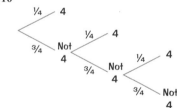

a) $\frac{3}{16}$ b) $\frac{37}{64}$

Q17 a)

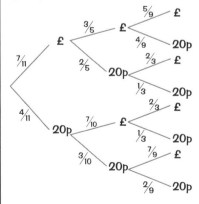

b) $\frac{28}{55}$ c) $\frac{46}{165}$

Q18 a) $\frac{1}{4}$
b) $\frac{1}{2}$ c) $\frac{1}{2}$

Q19 $\frac{1}{28}$